OXFORD*Playscripts*

Series editors: Steve Barlow and Steve Skidmore

Charlotte Brontë

adapted by Steve Barlow and Steve Skidmore

Jane Eyre

C000025209

OXFORD

UNIVERSITY PRESS

OXFORD

UNIVERSITY PRESS

Great Clarendon Street, Oxford OX2 6DP

Oxford University Press is a department of the University of Oxford.
It furthers the University's objective of excellence in research, scholarship,
and education by publishing worldwide in

Oxford New York

Athens Auckland Bangkok Bogotá Buenos Aires Calcutta Cape Town
Chennai Dar es Salaam Delhi Florence Hong Kong Istanbul Karachi
Kuala Lumpur Madrid Melbourne Mexico City Mumbai Nairobi
Paris São Paulo Singapore Taipei Tokyo Toronto Warsaw

with associated companies in Berlin Ibadan

Oxford is a registered trade mark of Oxford University Press
in the UK and in certain other countries

This adaptation of **Jane Eyre** © Steve Barlow and Steve Skidmore 1998
Activity section © Steve Barlow and Steve Skidmore 1998

First published 1998
Reprinted 1999

Printed and bound in Great Britain at Cambridge University Press

The publisher would like to thank the following for permission to
reproduce photographs:
pp 108, 109 Brontë Society, p 110 National Portrait Gallery /
Patrick Branwell Brontë, p 114 Mary Evans Picture Library (left),
The Salvation Army International Heritage Centre, p 119 Brontë
Society, p 121 Mary Evans Picture Library (left), Scope Picture
Library, p 127 Brontë Society

Illustrations are by Robert Goldsmith

Cover illustration by Simon Fell

ISBN 0 19 831296 2

Contents

Characters

In order of their appearance on stage:

Helen Burns	*a young, sickly girl who befriends Jane at Lowood School*
Miss Miller	*a strict teacher at Lowood School*
Miss Temple	*the superintendent at Lowood School, a kind and fair headmistress*
Mr Brocklehurst	*the manager of Lowood, a harsh, hypocritical man*
Jane Eyre	*an orphan, Jane is sent to Lowood School at ten years old; she leaves at eighteen to become a governess at Thornfield Hall*
Mrs Reed	*Jane's aunt, she spoils her own children, but detests Jane*
John Reed	*Jane's cousin; fourteen years old; an unpleasant bully*
Eliza Reed	*sister to John, a headstrong and selfish girl*
Georgina Reed	*younger sister to John and Eliza, pretty, but spiteful and spoilt*
Bessie	*Mrs Reed's servant*
Girl	*a pupil at Lowood*
Julia Severn	*a pupil at Lowood, with curly, red hair (non-speaking)*
Grace Poole	*a servant at Thornfield Hall*
Mrs Fairfax	*the housekeeper at Thornfield Hall, a fussy, but kindly woman*
Leah	*a servant at Thornfield Hall*
Adèle Varens	*a little French girl, Mr Rochester's ward and Jane's pupil*
Mr Rochester	*the master of Thornfield Hall*
John	*a servant at Thornfield Hall*
Lady Lynn	*a guest at Thornfield Hall; mother to Henry and Frederick*

Colonel Dent	*a guest at Thornfield Hall*
Henry Lynn **Frederick Lynn** }	*brothers, guests at Thornfield Hall*
Lady Ingram	*a guest at Thornfield Hall; mother of Blanche*
Mary Ingram	*her other daughter, also a guest*
Blanche Ingram	*a beautiful, young woman who is expected to marry Mr Rochester*
Gypsy	*a fortune teller who is not what she seems*
An Intruder	*who haunts Thornfield Hall (non-speaking)*
Mr Wood	*a clergyman*
Richard Mason	*a figure from Mr Rochester's past*
Mr Briggs	*a solicitor*
Bertha Mason	*a wild and violent woman*
Mary Rivers **Diana Rivers** }	*sisters living at Marsh End*
Hannah	*a servant at Marsh End*
St John Rivers	*a young clergyman, brother to Mary and Diana*
A Woman	*a woman whom Jane meets when she is hungry and homeless*
Rosamond Oliver	*a pretty heiress; in love with St John Rivers*
Publican	*at a public house close to Thornfield Hall*
Other Non-speaking Roles	*teachers and pupils at Lowood School (Act 1) servants at Thornfield Hall (Acts 2, 3 and 5)*

The characters of Jane Eyre and Eliza and Georgina Reed first appear as children in Act 1. In the rest of the play, they appear as adult women. A director may want to use different actors for the child and adult roles.

A Note on the Set

The play can be produced in a black box curtain set. As a rule, setting should be kept to a minimum. Where furniture is needed, it should be used to suggest a scene, rather than seek to recreate accurately the interior of a great house, or a schoolroom. For example, in the scenes at Thornfield Hall, a sofa or chaise-longue decorated with gilt or brocade, and one or two other items along these lines, will suggest wealth without filling the stage with needless objects. For outside scenes, the stage should be kept bare; here careful lighting can create the appropriate effects.

The staging of Act 5, Scene 1 requires some explanation. The stage should be split, with the fire and the accompanying action occupying one side, and perhaps the upstage area; while Jane and the publican play their part of the scene, in a small area downstage. They should both face the audience so that the publican is reliving the events and Jane is seeing them in her mind's eye. Sound effect levels will have to be carefully adjusted to allow the characters (particularly Jane and the publican) to be heard.

A Note on the Lighting

An asterisk (*) in the text indicates that information and advice about lighting can be found on this page.

Jane as Narrator
Whenever Jane speaks to the audience, she is stepping out of the action of the play to take the role of narrator. You might want to isolate Jane on these occasions using a spotlight. This will emphasize her figure and draw attention away from what is happening on the stage behind her.

The Red Room (Act 1, Scene 2)
Lighting is very important here. A deep red light creating as many shadows as possible will suggest an oppressive, spooky atmosphere. When Jane is first pushed into the Red Room, part of the stage should be lit red, with the rest lit in a more

naturalistic manner. This should give the impression that although Jane is in the Red Room, the door is still open and light from the rest of the house is still visible to her. (You could use a shuttered profile to create a shaft of light from an imaginary door.) When Mrs Reed or Bessie 'locks' the door, all other stage lighting should fade out, leaving Jane in a terrifying, red, supernatural world of her own terror.

The Chestnut Tree (Act 3, Scene 5)

The simplest way to create the effect of a large tree is by using gobos (metal cut-outs which fit inside profile-type lanterns) to project a pattern of leaves onto an appropriate background. Many patterned gobos are available ready-made; you will also need gobo holders. Contact your nearest theatre lighting hire and supply company for details. When ordering gobos, specify the type of lantern you intend to use as sizes differ.

The Fires at Thornfield Hall
(Act 3, Scene 4 and Act 5, Scene 1)

The first fire (in Mr Rochester's bedroom) should be quite a small affair; the stage should be dim, and a pulsing red light in the wing with a few bursts from a smoke machine will create the desired effect. Sound effects should be similarly low key.

The final fire (the destruction of Thornfield Hall) should be an altogether bigger affair, with much more intense red light and smoke from the wing to suggest the seat of the fire. Also, a larger stage area can be bathed in light from a flame projector. Your nearest theatre lighting hire and supply company will be able to advise you on what you need.

Act 1

· · · · · · ·

Scene 1

The schoolroom at Lowood School. The stage is set with benches and stools. The lights come up to reveal groups of girls, including **Helen Burns**, *who are plainly dressed. They are sitting eating a poor lunch of bread and cheese. There are teachers sitting with the girls, one of whom is* **Miss Miller**. *The atmosphere is subdued.* **Miss Temple**, *the headmistress, enters.*

Miss Temple　　　　All stand.

All the girls and teachers scramble hurriedly to their feet. **Mr Brocklehurst** *enters. He is a stern, harsh, man with no sense of humour, but a great sense of his own importance. He is leading* **Jane Eyre** *by the hand.* **Jane** *is miserable and frightened, but trying very hard not to show it.* **Mr Brocklehurst** *points to a stool.*

Mr Brocklehurst　　(*To Jane*) Fetch that stool.

Jane fetches the stool. It is heavy. **Mr Brocklehurst** *notices what the girls are eating. He ignores* **Jane**, *who stands holding the heavy stool, and moves sharply to the nearest girl. He snatches her bowl away. Holding the bowl at arm's length, he approaches Miss Temple.*

Mr Brocklehurst　　Miss Temple, these girls are eating bread and cheese. Bread and cheese, ma'am! What is the meaning of this... self-indulgence? This excess? This sinful gluttony?

Miss Temple　　　　I ordered the lunch to be served, Mr Brocklehurst. The cook had burnt the breakfast so badly that the girls could not eat it. As superintendent of this school, I decided...

Mr Brocklehurst	(*Interrupting*) As manager of this school, Miss Temple, I must remind you that these are charity girls; they must learn to accept their poverty without complaint. Madam, as the scriptures tell us, 'If ye suffer hunger or thirst for my sake, happy are ye!' When you put bread and cheese, instead of burnt porridge, into these children's mouths, you may indeed feed their vile bodies, but you starve their immortal souls!
Miss Temple	(*Coldly*) Your directions shall be attended to, Mr Brocklehurst.

> *Jane's arms grow tired and she drops the stool. The clatter draws **Mr Brocklehurst's** attention back to her.*

Mr Brocklehurst	A careless girl! Pick up the stool, child and stand upon it! (*Jane does so*) Miss Temple, teachers and children: you all see this girl? Her name is Jane Eyre. She is young. In her appearance she looks like an ordinary child. Who would have thought that the 'evil one' has already found a servant in her? It is my sad duty to warn you that you must be on your guard against this girl. Teachers, watch her. Girls, keep away from her; for this girl... I shudder to tell it... this girl is – a liar!

> *Jane looks straight ahead. The other girls whisper. The lights fade on the schoolroom. **Jane** speaks directly to the audience*.*

Jane	This was my introduction to Lowood School. Everyone had heard Mr Brocklehurst's accusation. They would all believe I was a liar. How could I prove otherwise? How could I ever hope to make friends, or win approval from my teachers? I felt as if I could die from grief and shame.

> *The lights come up again on the schoolroom. **Mr Brocklehurst** points at Jane.*

Mr Brocklehurst	Let her stand half an hour longer on that stool. No one is to speak to her for the rest of the day. Come, Miss Temple.

> *Mr Brocklehurst exits, followed by **Miss Temple**. The girls sit down and quietly begin to clear up their lunch bowls. One girl, **Helen Burns**, remains standing.*

*She deliberately walks over to Jane, squeezes her hand, and smiles. **Jane** returns her smile gratefully.*

Miss Miller   Burns! Burns! Did you not hear Mr Brocklehurst's instructions? You shall have nothing but bread and water tomorrow for your disobedience.

Helen   Yes, Miss Miller.

Helen returns to her group.

Miss Miller   And look at your apron. It is filthy! I shall make you wear the untidy badge... where is it?

Helen   I am wearing it already, Miss Miller.

Miss Miller   Then you shall wear it longer, Burns. Upon my word, you are a slovenly creature... hold out your hand.

*Helen holds out her hand and **Miss Miller** brings her cane down across it.*

Miss Miller   (*To all the girls*) Now, form lines! To the garden!

The girls get into lines and prepare to leave.

Miss Miller   Jane Eyre, you will remain where you are!

*Miss Miller signals to the girls, who exit in lines. They are followed by **Miss Miller** and any other teachers. **Jane** remains perfectly still until they have all gone. Then her face crumples and she begins to cry. Sobbing bitterly, she stumbles down from the stool and collapses in a heap on the floor. The lights fade on **Jane**.*

• •

Scene 2

*The schoolroom at Lowood; some time later. The lights come up to reveal **Jane** who lies curled in a heap on the floor. **Helen Burns** enters with a mug and some bread.*

Helen	I have brought you something to eat.

*Jane refuses to uncurl. **Helen** places the food and drink beside her. She takes a book from her pocket, sits down, and begins to read. After a few moments, **Jane** looks up. She looks at the mug and bread, uncurls, and takes a drink. **Helen** smiles at her.*

Jane	What book are you reading?
Helen	It is a book of philosophy.

Jane moves to sit beside Helen.

Jane	What is your name beside Burns?
Helen	Helen. (*She coughs*)
Jane	My name is Jane Eyre.

*Jane offers her hand; **Helen** shakes it solemnly.*

Jane	Do you come from far away?
Helen	Near the borders of Scotland.
Jane	You must want to leave Lowood.
Helen	No, why should I? I was sent to Lowood to get an education. It would be no use going away until I have done so.

Jane	But that teacher was so cruel to you.
Helen	Miss Miller? Cruel? Not at all! She dislikes my faults.
Jane	If I were you, I would dislike her. If she struck me with her cane, I would break it under her nose.
Helen	I'm sure you would do nothing of the sort; but if you did, Mr Brocklehurst would expel you from the school. Besides, the Bible tells us to return good for evil.
Jane	If we always obey those who are cruel and unjust, the wicked people will have it all their own way and grow worse and worse. When someone strikes us without a reason, we should strike back, hard enough to teach that person never to do it again.
Helen	I hope you will change your mind when you grow older.

She coughs again.

Jane	But it seems disgraceful to be beaten, and told off in front of a room full of people. I am far younger than you and I could not bear it.
Helen	We must all bear what it is our duty to bear.

Helen *coughs again. There is a pause as* **Jane** *thinks about this.*

Jane	How can you say you have faults? I think you are very good.
Helen	You must not judge by appearances. I am, as Miss Miller said, slovenly and careless. I forget rules; I read instead of learning my lessons. This upsets Miss Miller, who is always so neat and tidy…
Jane	(*Interrupting*) And cross and cruel! (*There is a pause*) Is Miss Temple as cross as Miss Miller?
Helen	Miss Temple is very good; it pains her to be severe to anyone, even the worst in the school. She corrects my faults gently, and praises me when I do well.

Jane	Does Miss Temple own the school?
Helen	I wish she did. Miss Temple is the superintendent. She has to answer to Mr Brocklehurst for all she does.
Jane	Mr Brocklehurst said we were charity girls. What is a charity girl?
Helen	We are all charity girls. Our schooling is paid for by charitable donations. I suppose you are an orphan.
Jane	My father and mother died before I can remember. Are you an orphan?
Helen	My mother is dead.
Jane	Are you happy here?

Helen coughs. For several moments, she cannot stop.

Jane	What's wrong? Helen? Shall I fetch someone?
Helen	No... I have a weak chest. I am used to it.

There is a pause.

Jane	Helen, why are you talking to me, when everybody thinks I am a liar?
Helen	Everybody, Jane? Fewer than thirty people heard you called a liar, and I am sure not one of those believes it.
Jane	After what Mr Brocklehurst said?
Helen	Mr Brocklehurst is not liked here. Besides, if all the world believed you were guilty, what does it matter as long as you knew you were in the right?
Jane	(*Passionately*) If no one loves me, I would rather die than live!
Helen	(*Calmly*) You think too much of the love of human beings.

Helen coughs again. The lights begin to fade.

Jane	Perhaps that is because I have known so little of it. How could I love Mrs Reed? Or her son John? When did they ever show affection for me?
Helen	Who is Mrs Reed?

> *The lights go out on the schoolroom.* **Helen** *remains sitting in the shadows.* **Jane** *steps forward to speak to the audience.*

Jane	As we sat in the deserted schoolroom, I told Helen Burns how I had passed my early years.
Mrs Reed	(*Off stage*) Jane Eyre, Jane Eyre! Where are you?

> **Mrs Reed, John, Eliza** *and* **Georgina Reed** *enter at the opposite side of the stage to* **Jane** *and Helen. The lights come up to reveal them in a tableau: the perfect family.* **Jane** *introduces them to the audience.*

Jane	Mrs Reed, widow of Mr Reed, magistrate, of Gateshead Hall. My aunt, and my guardian. Her daughters – Eliza: headstrong and selfish; and Georgina: pretty, spiteful and spoiled. Her son, John Reed: fourteen years old, and a bully.

> *Unseen by their mother,* **Eliza** *and* **Georgina** *pull faces at each other.*

Jane	Mrs Reed had always made it clear that she preferred to have the company of happy, contented little children. As she did not regard me as one of these, I spent a great deal of time alone. One afternoon, I was reading a book.

> **Jane** *moves to take the book off* **Helen** *and sits reading it.* **John** *approaches her.*

John Reed	There you are, Madam Mope!
Jane	What do you want?
John Reed	Say 'what do you want, Master Reed'. I want you to come here.

John beckons *Jane* to him. *Jane* puts down
the book, gets up, and speaks to Helen and
the audience.

Jane

John Reed was four years older than me. He ate too much,
which made him bilious and gave him flabby cheeks. He had
no affection for his mother or his sisters and only hate for me.
Every minute of every day he would punish me. The flesh on
my bones shrank when he came near. I was helpless against
him. No one heard my complaints. Mrs Reed never saw her
son strike me or heard him abuse me, though he did, both in
her presence and more frequently, behind her back.

Jane reluctantly moves towards *John*.

John Reed

That's right. (*He points*) Stand here.

John stares at *Jane*, then sticks his tongue
out at her. *Jane* remains completely still.
This continues for some time. Suddenly *John*
lashes out and strikes *Jane* on the side of her
head.

John Reed

That's for your impudence in answering back to Mamma and
for the look you've had in your eyes for the last two minutes,
you rat!

Jane stares at him, breathing deeply. *John*
points at the book.

John Reed

Show me the book.

Jane picks up the book and gives it to *John*.
He looks at it scornfully.

John Reed

You have no business to take our books. You have no money;
your father left you none. You ought to beg, and not live here
with gentleman's children like us. Now, I'll teach you to steal
from my bookshelves. Go and stand over there by the door.

Jane turns her back on *John* and starts to
walk away from him. *John* raises the book,
ready to throw it at *Jane*. At that moment,
Jane looks behind her.

Jane	No!

> *John freezes. **Jane** goes over to John, takes the book from his hand, and moves it in an arc, as if it were being thrown in slow motion.*

Jane	(*To the audience*) But I wasn't quick enough. The volume was flung; it hit me. (*She drops the book*) I fell, striking my head against the door.

> ***Jane** puts her flat hand against her head, takes it away and reacts as if she sees blood on the palm of her hand.*

Jane	Blood!

> ***John** comes out of his freeze as **Jane** shouts at him.*

Jane	Wicked and cruel boy! You are like a murderer! You are like a slave driver! You are like the Roman emperors!
John Reed	(*Furious*) What! What! Did you say that to me? Wait 'til I tell Mother, but first…

> *He rushes at Jane.*

Jane	Murderer! Nero! Caligula!
John Reed	Rat! Rat!

> ***Jane** lashes out at John. The fury of her attack startles and frightens him and he cowers away, howling.*

John Reed	Ow!

> ***Mrs Reed**, followed by **Eliza** and **Georgina**, rush across to where **Jane** and **John** are fighting.*

Mrs Reed	(*To Jane*) How dare you! (*Calling off stage*) Bessie! Bessie, help!

> *Bessie enters and drags **Jane** away from John.*

Bessie What a fury to fly at Master John!

Mrs Reed Did ever anybody see such a picture of passion!

> ***Jane** is subdued and stands panting. **Bessie** holds her firmly.*

Mrs Reed (*To Bessie*) Take her away to the Red Room and lock her in there!

> ***John**, **Eliza** and **Georgina Reed** exit.*

Jane (*To Helen and the audience; calmly*) I resisted all the way. (*She struggles furiously as she shouts at Bessie*) No! No! Leave me alone! Get off me!

Bessie For shame, to strike a young gentleman, your young master!

Jane Master! How is he my master? Am I a servant?

Mrs Reed No. You are less than a servant, for you do nothing for your keep.

Bessie (*To Mrs Reed*) She never did such a thing before.

Mrs Reed But it was always in her. She's an underhand little thing.

Bessie (*To Jane*) You ought to be aware, miss, that you are under obligations to Mrs Reed. She keeps you; if she were to send you away, you would have to go to the poorhouse.

Mrs Reed You should not think yourself equal with my children. They will have a great deal of money and you will have none. If you make yourself useful and pleasant, then, perhaps, you should have a home here. But if you become passionate and rude, I shall send you away.

> ***Mrs Reed** mimes opening a door. The stage is suddenly covered in red light★ to create the Red Room.*

*Bessie pulls **Jane** into the Red Room, fetches a stool and pushes **Jane** onto it.*

Bessie   There sit down, and think of your wickedness.

*Jane immediately springs up from the stool, but is thrust down again by **Mrs Reed**.*

Mrs Reed   Sit still, girl. (*Jane continues to struggle*) Bessie, tie her to the stool.

Bessie   (*At a loss*) What with, ma'am?

Mrs Reed   For heaven's sake, girl! Use your garters, if you've nothing else.

Bessie turns her back on the audience and prepares to take her garters off in order to tie Jane to the stool.

Jane   (*Giving in*) Don't take them off! I will not stir.

Mrs Reed and Bessie freeze as Jane describes the Red Room to the audience.

Jane   The Red Room was a spare bedchamber; never slept in, but the grandest room in the house. Red curtains, red carpet, pink walls and darkly polished old mahogany furniture everywhere. There was a bed supported by massive pillars, wardrobes, tables, and chairs: all mahogany. It had been my uncle Reed's room. It had not been used since his death.

Bessie and Mrs Reed come out of their freeze.

Bessie   Say your prayers, Miss Eyre, when you are by yourself; for if you don't repent, something bad might come down the chimney and take you away!

Bessie and Mrs Reed move away as if leaving the Red Room. Mrs Reed mimes locking the door behind her. She and Bessie exit. The red light becomes stronger and more sinister.

Jane	(*Calling out*) Aunt Reed… let me out, please. My head aches, I think I'm ill. It's getting dark. Please, I don't want to be in here. I'm frightened! My uncle Reed died in this room. You promised him you would treat me kindly. You have not! You have treated me cruelly and locked me in this dreadful room. (*She glances round wildly*) Who's there? No! No! (*She screams*) Let me out, let me out, let me out!

> *Jane screams, on and on. **Bessie** rushes on stage and mimes unlocking the door of the Red Room. As she moves towards Jane, the red light becomes weaker. **Jane** grabs **Bessie's** hand.*

Bessie	Miss Eyre, are you ill?
Jane	(*Hysterical*) Take me out. Let me go into the nursery!
Bessie	What for? Are you hurt? Have you seen something?
Jane	My uncle Reed…
Bessie	Your uncle's dead.
Jane	I saw him! I was thinking that the spirits of the dead might rise from the grave to punish anyone who disobeyed their last wishes, and I looked at the bed, and there he was…

> *Jane bursts into terrified sobs. **Mrs Reed** enters.*

Mrs Reed	What is all this? Bessie, I believe I gave orders that Jane Eyre should be left in the Red Room until I came to her myself.
Bessie	She screamed so loud, ma'am.
Mrs Reed	Let her go. (*To Jane*) You cannot succeed in getting out of here by trickery. I hate deceit, particularly in children. You will now stay here an hour longer…
Jane	(*Pleading*) Oh aunt! Have pity. Forgive me! I cannot endure it. Let me be punished some other way! I shall die if…
Mrs Reed	(*Interrupting*) Silence! (*To Bessie*) Leave her. Lock the door.

*Mrs Reed moves away from Bessie and
Jane, as if leaving the room. Bessie
hesitates, but dare not disobey. She too moves
away from Jane, who continues to sob
brokenly. Bessie pauses, as if in the
doorway to the room, and turns back to
Jane.*

Jane Bessie, please… don't do this… I beg you… please…

*Bessie mimes locking the door. Immediately,
the red light floods back, even more strongly
than before. Bessie and Mrs Reed exit.
Jane turns slowly to look at the 'bed', reacts
as if she has again seen her uncle's ghost, and
faints in sheer terror. Blackout.*

*Jane moves to sit facing Helen. The lights
come up on Jane and Helen in the
schoolroom at Lowood. Jane speaks to Helen
and the audience.*

Jane When I awoke, I felt weak, and sick, and miserable. For some
weeks I stayed in the nursery, never going out, and seeing no
one but Bessie. One day, Mrs Reed sent for me.

*The lights dim on the schoolroom and Helen
and come up on another part of the stage.
Bessie enters.*

Bessie Come along, Miss Jane, all this moping about isn't going to
help you or anyone else. (*Jane moves towards Bessie*) Take off
your pinafore. Look smart about it.

*Bessie helps Jane to take off her pinafore
and tidy her hair. Mrs Reed and Mr
Brocklehurst enter. Bessie moves to one
side.*

Mrs Reed This is the little girl I wrote to you about, Mr Brocklehurst:
Jane Eyre.

Mr Brocklehurst inspects Jane closely.

Mr Brocklehurst	Her size is small; what is her age?
Mrs Reed	Ten years.
Mr Brocklehurst	Well, Jane Eyre, are you a good child?

Jane bows her head.

Mrs Reed	(*Shaking her head*) Perhaps the less said on that matter, the better.
Mr Brocklehurst	I am sorry to hear it! She and I must have some talk. (*He speaks directly to Jane*) There is no sight so sad as that of a naughty little girl. Do you know where the wicked go after death?

Jane looks up.

Jane	They go to hell.
Mr Brocklehurst	And what is hell? Can you tell me that?
Jane	A pit full of fire.
Mr Brocklehurst	And should you like to fall into that pit, and to be burning there for ever?
Jane	No, sir.
Mr Brocklehurst	What must you do to avoid it?

Jane thinks about the answer for a moment.

Jane	I must keep in good health, and not die.

Mr Brocklehurst winces at this answer. Bessie has to stop herself laughing and Mrs Reed looks furious.

Mr Brocklehurst	Do you read your Bible?
Jane	Sometimes.
Mr Brocklehurst	Do you like the psalms?

Jane	No, sir. Psalms are not interesting.
Mr Brocklehurst	That proves you have a wicked heart, and you must pray God to give you a new and clean one.
Mrs Reed	Mr Brocklehurst, I would be glad if the superintendent and teachers at Lowood School would keep a strict eye on this girl. She is deceitful.

Jane is hurt by the unfairness of Mrs Reed's comments. She tries hard not to cry. Mr Brocklehurst turns to Mrs Reed.

Mr Brocklehurst	Deceit is a sad fault in a child. She will be watched, Mrs Reed. I will speak to Miss Temple and the teachers.
Mrs Reed	I would wish her to be made useful and to be kept humble.
Mr Brocklehurst	Be assured, she will, Mrs Reed. Indeed, only the other day my daughter visited the school, and on her return she exclaimed, 'Oh dear Papa, how quiet and plain the girls at Lowood look; they are almost like poor people's children! They looked at my dress as if they had never seen a silk gown before!'

Mr Brocklehurst turns back to Jane, takes a pamphlet from his pocket, and gives it to her.

Mr Brocklehurst	Little girl, here is a book entitled 'The Child's Guide'. Read it with prayer – especially that part containing 'an account of the awfully sudden death of Martha G, a naughty child addicted to falsehood and deceit'. (*To Mrs Reed*) I bid you good day, ma'am.

> *Bessie shows **Mr Brocklehurst** off stage.*
> ***Mrs Reed** watches them go. **Jane** looks at*
> *the pamphlet, then at Mrs Reed. She is*
> *furious. **Mrs Reed** turns back to **Jane** and*
> *catches her look of hatred.*

Mrs Reed   Go out of the room. Go into the nursery.

> ***Jane** starts to leave, but then pauses for a*
> *moment and turns back to face Mrs Reed.*

Jane   (*Angrily*) I am not deceitful. If I were, I would say I loved you; but I declare I hate you more than anybody in the world except John Reed. And this book about the liar, (*She throws it down*) you may give to Georgina, for it is she who tells lies, and not I.

> ***Mrs Reed** and **Jane** stand staring at each*
> *other.*

Mrs Reed   (*After a pause*) Do you have anything else to say?

Jane   I will never call you aunt again as long as I live. If anyone asks me how you took care of me, I shall say you treated me with miserable cruelty.

Mrs Reed   (*Angrily*) How dare you say that, Jane Eyre.

Jane   How dare I? Because it is the truth. You think I have no feelings, and that I can live without one bit of love or kindness; but I cannot. What would Uncle Reed say if he were alive?

Mrs Reed   What?

Jane   My uncle Reed is in heaven and can see all you do and think; and so can my papa and mamma. They know how you shut me up all day long and wish me dead. People think you are a good woman, but you are really bad and hard-hearted. You are deceitful! Send me to school soon, Mrs Reed, for I hate living here.

*Jane stares hard at Mrs Reed. **Mrs Reed** is the first to drop her gaze. Defeated, **Mrs Reed** exits. The lights come up on **Helen** and the schoolroom. **Jane** turns and speaks to Helen.*

Jane

And so I came to Lowood. Well, is not Mrs Reed a hard-hearted, bad woman?

Helen

What an impression she has left upon your heart! Life is too short to be spent in remembering every injustice. Life is soon over, and there is a better world beyond this one.

*Miss Temple enters. **Helen** stands up. **Jane** moves to join her.*

Miss Temple

I came on purpose to find you, Jane Eyre. Have you cried your grief away?

Jane

I am afraid I shall never do that.

Miss Temple

Why?

Jane

Because I have been wrongly accused; and you, ma'am, and everybody else will now think that I am wicked.

Miss Temple

We shall think you are what you prove yourself to be, my child. I shall hear your story, and make my own enquiries. If you are innocent, everyone shall know it. (*She smiles at Jane*) I know it already.

Helen

And so do I.

*Jane smiles at Miss Temple, then, impulsively, she hugs **Helen**.*

Miss Temple

And how are you tonight, Helen? Have you coughed much today?

Helen

Not quite so much, I think, ma'am.

Miss Temple

And the pain in your chest?

Helen

It is a little better.

Miss Temple	Good. You are to read from the Bible at prayers tomorrow, are you not? Have you chosen a verse yet?
Helen	Yes, ma'am. From the 'Book of Isaiah'. (*She closes her eyes to remember the verse, and quotes*) 'Watchman, what of the night? Watchman, what of the night? The watchman said, "The morning cometh, and also the night".'

> *Helen opens her eyes and smiles at Miss Temple. **Miss Temple** catches her breath sharply, and seems on the verge of tears. She hurriedly turns away and exits. **Jane** reaches out and takes **Helen's** hand. A **girl** enters.*

Girl	Helen Burns, Miss Miller says if you don't go and tidy your work away this minute, there will be trouble!

> *The **girl** exits. **Helen** sighs and follows her. The lights dim.*

· ·

Scene 3

> *The schoolroom at Lowood; it is several weeks later. The stage is dark. Girls (including **Helen**) are sitting on benches, in rows, working with teachers and senior pupils. **Jane** steps forward to speak to the audience.*

Jane	Over the next few weeks, Helen and I became firm friends. I worked hard at my lessons and would almost have enjoyed being at Lowood, except that Mr Brocklehurst's accusation that I was a liar cast a gloom upon my heart.

> *The lights come up as **Jane** takes her place on a bench. Everyone stands as **Miss Temple** enters.*

Miss Temple	Good morning, school.
Everyone	Good morning, Miss Temple.

Miss Temple	Before you continue with your lessons, I have an announcement to make. I have investigated the accusations made by Mr Brocklehurst against Jane Eyre, and I have found them to be false. Jane Eyre is not a liar.

> *There is general rejoicing.* **Miss Miller** *shakes hands with* **Jane.** **Miss Temple** *kisses her.* **Jane** *exchanges hugs with one or two friends.* **Mr Brocklehurst** *enters upon this scene; the atmosphere changes immediately. The girls stand silent with downcast eyes. The teachers become wooden.*

Mr Brocklehurst	Miss Temple, ladies, children.
Everyone	Good morning, Mr Brocklehurst.

> **Mr Brocklehurst** *paces around the schoolroom, scanning the rows of girls. He stops still, in a state of shock. He approaches one girl,* **Julia Severn,** *and takes hold of her hair in a shaking hand.*

Mr Brocklehurst	Miss Temple, what – what is this girl with curled hair? Red hair, ma'am, curled – all over?
Miss Temple	It is Julia Severn.
Mr Brocklehurst	And why, despite all my instructions, is her hair one mass of curls?
Miss Temple	Julia's hair curls naturally.
Mr Brocklehurst	Naturally? We are not slaves to nature. Miss Temple, this girl's hair must be cut off. Turn around, all of you.

> *The girls all turn so that they face away from Mr Brocklehurst. He inspects the hair of one or two.*

Mr Brocklehurst	All these girls must have their hair cut off.
Miss Temple	(*Exasperated*) Mr Brocklehurst…

Mr Brocklehurst	(*Interrupting*) Miss Temple, moderation and meekness must be our watchwords. Fine clothes and braided hair are vanities, and an abomination in the sight of the Lord…

> *One of the girls faints. Other girls gather round her excitedly.* **Miss Temple** *hurries over and examines her.*

Mr Brocklehurst	What is the matter with the girl? Miss Temple, I hope you are not going to reward such a display of weakness with undue attention…
Miss Temple	(*Sharply*) Mr Brocklehurst, kindly be silent!

> **Miss Temple's** *tone of voice shocks Mr Brocklehurst. He remains silent.*

Miss Temple	Miss Miller, please fetch the doctor as quickly as you can.
Miss Miller	What is it?
Miss Temple	I believe it may be typhoid.

> **Miss Miller** *is shocked and exits quickly.* **Mr Brocklehurst** *claps a handkerchief to his mouth and rushes off stage. The rest freeze as* **Jane** *steps forward and speaks to the audience. The lights fade on the schoolroom. During the following speech, the girls,* **Miss Temple** *and the teachers leave the stage.* **Helen** *remains. A small bed is brought on, and she climbs into it.*

Jane	Typhoid fever had crept upon the semi-starved orphans of Lowood School. Over half my fellow pupils became ill. Some went home, only to die there. Some with no homes died at the school, and were buried quickly and quietly. Spring turned to summer; those of us who remained well had no lessons. We were happy roaming the woods and fields as we liked. Mr Brocklehurst never came near Lowood now. We had enough to eat: there were fewer to feed, and the sick could eat little. The one great sorrow of my life now, was that Helen was sick. She had not caught typhoid. Her illness was consumption.

Jane	At first, in my ignorance, I thought she was in no danger and would soon recover. I was not allowed to visit Helen, but one evening, while Miss Temple was busy elsewhere, I crept into the room where she lay.

*The lights come up on the bed. As **Jane** approaches, **Helen** sits up.*

Helen	Jane? Why have you come here? It must be late.
Jane	I came to see you, Helen. I couldn't sleep until I had spoken to you.
Helen	You have come to bid me goodbye then.
Jane	Why, Helen? Are you going home?
Helen	(*Looking heavenwards*) Yes, to my last home.

*Jane realizes what **Helen** is saying.*

Jane	(*Shocked*) No, no, Helen.

*Helen takes **Jane's** hand.*

Helen	You are cold. Lie down and cover yourself with my quilt.

Jane does so.

Helen	I am very happy, Jane. When you hear that I am dead, don't be sad. By dying young, I shall escape great sufferings.
Jane	Where are you going to, Helen? Can you see? Do you know?
Helen	I believe; I have faith. I am going to God.
Jane	And shall I see you again, Helen, when I die?

Helen smiles and lies back.

Helen	I feel as if I could sleep. Don't leave me, Jane.
Jane	I won't.

Jane settles down to sleep as the lights fade. There is a pause. Miss Temple enters. She feels for the pulse in Helen's neck. She does not find it. She gently wakes Jane.

Miss Temple Jane. Jane, wake up now.

Jane (*Sleepily*) Miss Temple... is it morning? (**Miss Temple** *helps her to get up*) I'm sorry... I mustn't wake Helen.

Miss Temple Jane... Helen is dead.

The lights slowly fade to blackout.

• •

Act 2

·······

Scene 1

Thornfield Hall. The stage is set with a comfortable sofa, a chair, a footstool, and a small table bearing one or two books. The lights come up on **Grace Poole** *who is sitting on the sofa. She looks around, cautiously, and then takes out a small black bottle from her pocket and drinks. The sound of a carriage is heard off stage. As it draws to a halt,* **Grace Poole** *puts the stopper back in the bottle, puts it back in her pocket and exits quickly. We hear the voices of* **Jane** *(now eighteen years old) and* **Mrs Fairfax** *from off stage.*

Mrs Fairfax   (*Off stage*) You must be Jane Eyre. How do you do, my dear?

Jane   (*Off stage*) Mrs Fairfax?

Mrs Fairfax   (*Off stage*) That's right. Do come in and sit down.

Jane *and* **Mrs Fairfax** *enter.* **Mrs Fairfax** *guides* **Jane** *to sit on the sofa and begins to remove her shawl and untie her bonnet strings in a fussy, but kindly way.*

Mrs Fairfax   Have you come all the way from Lowood today? (*Jane nods*) You must be exhausted, poor thing.

Jane   Please don't trouble…

Mrs Fairfax   Oh, it is no trouble, I am sure your hands must be quite numb with cold.

She puts Jane's bonnet and shawl to one side and calls off stage.

Mrs Fairfax   Leah! Leah!

Leah enters.

Leah	Yes, Mrs Fairfax?
Mrs Fairfax	Take my keys and cut a sandwich or two for Miss Eyre (*Leah turns to go*)... and a little wine, I think... (*Leah waits for more instructions*) ...well, what are you waiting for, girl, off with you. (*Leah exits*) Now, Miss Eyre, you have your luggage with you I suppose?
Jane	Yes, ma'am.
Mrs Fairfax	I'll see it is taken to your room.

> *There is a slight, embarrassed pause as both **Jane** and **Mrs Fairfax** try to think of something to say next.*

Mrs Fairfax	Were you at Lowood long, Miss Eyre?
Jane	(*Nodding*) Eight years. First as a pupil, and then as a teacher.
Mrs Fairfax	You must have been there during that dreadful typhoid outbreak. My late husband told me all about it at the time. He was angry that the school had been neglected. He said it was all the fault of some man called Bricklebank, or some such name...
Jane	Mr Brocklehurst.
Mrs Fairfax	That was it! I wonder you stayed there so long.
Jane	After the fever had passed, the trustees insisted that the superintendent, Miss Temple, should have more freedom to run the school. It became a much happier place. Indeed, I did not think to leave it, but then Miss Temple married...
Mrs Fairfax	And you decided to change your situation. Quite right. When I saw your advertisement in the newspaper, I knew at once you would be just the person we needed... oh, goodness, where is Leah with that tray? Excuse me, Miss Eyre.

> *Mrs Fairfax exits. Jane waits, a little nervously. She stands and moves about the stage, looking at her new surroundings.*

*For somewhere off stage there comes a burst of low and horrible laughter. **Jane** gives a start. The laughter is heard again. From off stage comes the sound of running feet.*
***Adèle Varens** enters at speed, races up to the astonished **Jane**, and impulsively hugs her.*

Adèle   Mademoiselle, vous êtes ma nouvelle gouvernante?
(Are you my new governess?)

***Mrs Fairfax** returns.*

Mrs Fairfax   Adèle, what are you doing here? I told you most distinctly that I would not have Miss Eyre bothered as soon as she stepped through the door…

Adèle   (*Ignoring her*) Bonsoir, mademoiselle. Je m'appelle Adèle Varens.
(Good evening, miss. I am Adèle Varens.)

Jane   Bonsoir, Adèle. Je suis enchantée de faire ta connaissance.

Adèle   (*Delighted*) Ah! Vous parlez ma langue aussi couramment que Monsieur Rochester, enfin!

Mrs Fairfax   Stop, stop! Oh my. (*To Jane*) Can you understand her when she gabbles on so fast?

Jane   Yes, indeed. I said I was pleased to meet her and she was kind enough to say I spoke French as well as Mr Rochester. But she asked whether I was her governess… I understood I was to be governess to Miss Fairfax.

Mrs Fairfax   Miss Fairfax? Oh, no my dear, I have no family. Adèle is Mr Rochester's ward.

Adèle   Mademoiselle, est-ce que vous desirez…

Mrs Fairfax   Adèle, in English, if you please!

Adèle   Shall I sing for you now, miss? Or dance? Or speak poetry?

Mrs Fairfax   You can go to your room for Miss Eyre, Adèle, and let her get over her journey before you pester her any more.

| Jane | Je suis un peu fatiguée à ce moment, Adèle. |
| | (I am rather tired at the moment, Adèle.) |

| Adèle | Oui, mademoiselle. A bientôt. |
| | (Yes, miss. I will see you soon.) |

Adèle curtsies and exits. Leah enters with the wine and sandwiches, puts them down on the small table, and exits. Mrs Fairfax fusses with them.

| Jane | Mrs Fairfax, who is Mr Rochester? |

| Mrs Fairfax | Why, Mr Rochester is the owner of Thornfield. |

| Jane | I thought this house belonged to you. |

| Mrs Fairfax | Bless you, child, what an idea! I am only the housekeeper. |

| Jane | And when shall I see Mr Rochester? |

| Mrs Fairfax | Why, my dear, I hardly know. Mr Rochester visits rarely, and always when we least expect him. |

| Jane | What sort of man is he? |

| Mrs Fairfax | He has travelled a very great deal. I dare say he is clever, but I cannot always be sure when he is pleased or angry, or whether he is being serious or not. At any rate, he is a very good master. |

| Jane | Mrs Fairfax, just before Adèle came in, I heard someone laugh. It was a most peculiar laugh, very loud. Did you hear it? |

| Mrs Fairfax | That would be Grace Poole, one of the servants. She and Leah are sometimes noisy together. |

The laughter is heard again. Mrs Fairfax calls crossly off stage.

| Mrs Fairfax | Grace! Leah! |

	After a pause, **Grace Poole** *enters, followed by* **Leah.**
Mrs Fairfax	Too much noise, Grace. Remember Mr Rochester's orders. (*Turning to Jane*) Now, Miss Eyre, Leah will show you to your room.
Jane	Thank you, it has been a tiring day. Goodnight, Mrs Fairfax.
Mrs Fairfax	Goodnight, my dear.
	Jane exits with **Leah.**
Grace Poole	(*To Mrs Fairfax*) Doesn't she know?
Mrs Fairfax	Mr Rochester gave express orders that she should not.
Grace Poole	Tha'd happen get nobody to take the job on if they did.
Mrs Fairfax	That will do, Grace. Attend to your duties.
	Mrs Fairfax *exits.* **Grace Poole** *watches her go, shrugs, and takes a drink, defiantly, from her secret bottle. Blackout.*

. . . .

Scene 2

	The lights come up on **Jane.** *Behind her, the stage is dark and empty. She speaks to the audience.*
Jane	I settled quickly into life at Thornfield Hall. I was pleased to find that Mrs Fairfax was no great lady, but a kindly widow. My duties were not hard; my pupil, Adèle, was affectionate and eager to please. Indeed, after some weeks, I began to wish that something would happen to break the regular pattern of my new life. One evening, I set off for the nearby village to post a letter. The ground was hard and icy, the air was still, the road was lonely. I walked a mile from Thornfield. As darkness fell, the moon rose and a mist began to form.

The sound of hoofbeats is heard off stage. As Jane speaks to the audience, it grows rapidly louder.

Jane   As I turned back, I heard the clatter of hooves in the lane. Moonlight and mist reminded me of Bessie's nursery tales of phantom horses. The hooves echoed eerily between the steep banks of the lane, and suddenly a great horse burst out of the bank of fog and reared before me!

*The sound of the hoofbeats changes from a gallop to a frantic clatter. **Mr Rochester** enters unseen, and takes up his position in the dark. A horse neighs. **Jane** cowers away. There is a cry in the darkness and the sound of a rider falling. The hoofbeats die away. **Jane** looks up cautiously. From the darkness, a voice speaks.*

Mr Rochester   Damnation!

*The lights come up to reveal **Mr Rochester** sprawled on the stage, clutching at his ankle. He is obviously in some pain and very annoyed.*

Jane	Are you injured, sir?

Mr Rochester gives her a disgusted look, tries to stand, and sinks back down with a groan.

Jane	Can I do anything?
Mr Rochester	Ha! An elf frightens my horse and then offers assistance. A most obliging sprite!
Jane	I am no elf or sprite, sir.
Mr Rochester	Then you can help me up.

Jane helps Mr Rochester to stand.

Mr Rochester	You had better be off home. It is late.
Jane	I am not at all afraid of being out late, when it is moonlight. I cannot think of leaving you alone, sir, till I see that you are fit to mount your horse.
Mr Rochester	Oh? And what could you do?
Jane	Run over to the village for you if you are hurt, sir, or fetch help from Thornfield…
Mr Rochester	I shall survive; it is only a sprain. And what is Thornfield? That house with the battlements?
Jane	Yes, sir.
Mr Rochester	Whose house is it?
Jane	Mr Rochester's.
Mr Rochester	Do you know Mr Rochester?
Jane	I have never seen him, sir. I have not been at Thornfield long.
Mr·Rochester	Then he is not at home – do you know where he is?
Jane	I do not.

Mr Rochester	And what do you do at Thornfield? You are not dressed as a servant.
Jane	I am the new governess.
Mr Rochester	The governess! I had forgotten. Well, governess, will you hand me my whip? It lies there under the hedge.

Jane hands Mr Rochester his whip.

Mr Rochester	Now, if you will be so good as to help me...

Mr Rochester puts his hand on Jane's shoulder to support himself.

Mr Rochester	You will not lead me to one of your faery hills, and put me to sleep for a hundred years?
Jane	No, sir. I shall lead you to your horse, and then I shall post my letter.

Mr Rochester laughs. Jane helps him off stage. The lights fade as they go.

· ·

Scene 3

Thornfield Hall as before. As the lights come up, a flustered Mrs Fairfax is giving orders to Leah. Jane enters.

Mrs Fairfax	Leah! Light a fire in the drawing room, and air the sheets in the master bedroom. (*Leah exits*) Oh dear, what a to-do. We hear nothing from him for six months and then without a word of warning... (*She sees Jane*) Ah, Miss Eyre, there you are. The master has been asking for you.
Jane	The master?
Mrs Fairfax	Mr Rochester, to be sure. He rode in half an hour ago. He wants to see you and Adèle directly.

*Adèle enters, in a rush, and makes straight for Jane. During the following dialogue, **Mr Rochester** enters, walking with a stick. **Jane** and **Adèle** do not notice him. **Mrs Fairfax** approaches him, but he waves her to silence. She obeys, and sits down.*

Adèle   Mademoiselle, Monsieur Rochester est revenu…

Jane   Adèle! In English, please.

*Adèle pouts but does as **Jane** tells her.*

Adèle   Mr Rochester has come back! He says he has a present for me in his 'bagages', and perhaps one for you too. He asked me the name of my new governess, and whether she was a small person, who is… (*She searches for the correct word*)… sin.

Jane   (*Amused*) Thin, Adèle.

Adèle   Ah, oui, thin… and pale, and I said 'yes', because you are, aren't you?

Mr Rochester   Do you recognize yourself from that flattering description, Miss Eyre?

*Jane recognizes Mr Rochester's voice and turns in surprise. Then she quickly recovers herself and bows. **Adèle** flies to Mr Rochester.*

Adèle   Mon cadeau, monsieur, et cela de Mademoiselle Eyre?
(Where is my present, sir, and Miss Eyre's?)

Mr Rochester   What's all this about cadeaux? Did you expect a present, Miss Eyre? Are you fond of presents?

Mr Rochester limps forward and sits down.

Jane   I have little experience of them, sir. They are generally thought to be agreeable things.

Mr Rochester   Humph! (*He indicates that Jane should sit down too*). And where do you come from, Miss Eyre?

Jane	(*Sitting*) From Lowood School.
Mr Rochester	I have heard of it. How long were you there?
Jane	Eight years.
Mr Rochester	Enough to undermine any constitution! No wonder you have the look of another world. Who are your parents?
Jane	I have none.
Mr Rochester	I thought not. Then you were waiting for your people out there in the lane?
Jane	My people, sir?
Mr Rochester	The elves, the faery folk. It's a proper moonlit evening for them to be out.
Jane	(*Smiling slightly*) The men in green all left England a hundred years ago. I don't think either summer, or harvest, or winter moon will ever shine on their dances any more.

Mrs Fairfax looks between Jane and Mr Rochester, obviously completely baffled by this conversation.

Mr Rochester	(*Impatiently to Mrs Fairfax*) Madam, I should like some tea.
Mrs Fairfax	(*Rising from her seat*) Come along, Adèle, time for bed.

Mrs Fairfax exits with Adèle.

Mr Rochester	The director of Lowood is a Mr Brocklehurst, is it not?
Jane	Yes, sir.
Mr Rochester	And I suppose you and the other girls all worshipped him.
Jane	(*Quickly and sharply*) Oh, no!
Mr Rochester	A forthright answer!

Jane	Mr Brocklehurst is a harsh and pompous man. He cut off our hair, and gave us burnt porridge to eat and blunt needles to sew. He bored us with long lectures and frightened us with talk of hell until we were afraid to go to bed.
Mr Rochester	What age were you when you went to Lowood?
Jane	About ten.
Mr Rochester	And you stayed there eight years; then you are now eighteen. (*Jane nods*) And what did you learn at Lowood, Miss Eyre? Do you play the piano?
Jane	A little, sir.
Mr Rochester	So might any schoolgirl say. Play, then. There, (*He indicates off stage with his hand*) in the library.

Jane exits. We hear the sound of her playing a piano off stage. **Mrs Fairfax** *enters. She listens to the music with some pleasure.* **Mr Rochester** *also listens for a moment, then he calls off stage.*

Mr Rochester	Enough!

The music stops. **Jane** *enters and waits.*

Mr Rochester	You play a little, I see, but not well. Do you have any other… (*ironically*) accomplishments, Miss Eyre?
Jane	(*Annoyed*) I paint, sir.
Mr Rochester	I have touched a nerve, I see. Well, show me.

Jane fetches her portfolio from off stage. **Mr Rochester** *examines the paintings. He is impressed, despite himself.*

Mr Rochester	Now, these have taken much time and some thought. Where did you find the images?
Jane	Out of my head.

Mr Rochester	Has it more of the same inside it?
Jane	More… and better, I hope.
Mr Rochester	Were you happy when you painted these pictures?
Jane	Yes… yes, I was.
Mr Rochester	And are you satisfied with them?
Jane	Far from it. The contrast between what I imagine, and what I can set down on paper, leaves me in despair.
Mr Rochester	Yet these are strange paintings for a schoolgirl. These are scenes you must have seen in a dream… and who taught you to paint the wind? Well! (*He puts the drawings down and stands suddenly*) I have ridden far today. I wish you goodnight, Miss Eyre.

*Mr Rochester limps off, passing **Leah** who enters, bringing his tea. He ignores her completely. **Leah** watches him go, then, with a sigh, also exits.*

Jane	(*To Mrs Fairfax*) Is Mr Rochester always so strange and abrupt?
Mrs Fairfax	Is he? I am so used to him, I hardly notice it. He has not always had… an easy life. I don't think he has lived at Thornfield for more than two weeks together since he inherited the estate… and no wonder.
Jane	No wonder? What do you mean, Mrs Fairfax? Why should he avoid Thornfield?
Mrs Fairfax	(*Turning away from Jane*) Perhaps he thinks it is gloomy. Goodnight, my dear.

Mrs Fairfax exits. Jane gazes after her in puzzlement, as the lights fade.

. . . .

Scene 4

Thornfield Hall; some weeks later.
*The lights come up on **Jane** who speaks to*
the audience.

Jane But days passed, and then weeks, and Mr Rochester did not leave Thornfield Hall. He often sought me out, and I became used to his moods. I began to enjoy his company and conversation, harsh though it sometimes was. One day, his long-awaited luggage arrived and Adèle at last received her precious 'cadeau'.

*The lights brighten. **Jane** picks up a book, sits down on the sofa, and begins to read. She stands quickly as **Adèle** enters carrying a gift-wrapped parcel, closely followed by **Mr Rochester**.*

Adèle (*Excitedly*) Ma boîte! Ma boîte!

Mr Rochester Your 'boîte' indeed. Now disembowel it in silence, if you please.

***Adèle** rips the parcel open to reveal a very elaborate dress.*

Adèle Oh ciel! Que c'est beau! Mademoiselle Eyre, regardez!
(Oh, heavens! How beautiful it is! Look, Miss Eyre!)

*She rushes off stage with her parcel while **Mr Rochester** turns his attention to **Jane**.*

Mr Rochester Sit down, Miss Eyre... if you please, that is. Confound it, I am constantly forgetting to be polite.

***Jane** smiles and sits down. **Mr Rochester** sits down too.*

Mr Rochester You examine me, Miss Eyre. Do you think me handsome?

Jane Oh, no, sir.

Mr Rochester No, sir! A good round answer. And what fault do you find with me, pray? (***Jane** says nothing*) You are not pretty, any more than I am handsome.(*Jane looks down, embarrassed*) Ah! You are silent, Miss Eyre. Do I annoy you?

Jane

You are rather abrupt, sir.

Mr Rochester

And do you not think that my age and experience give me the right to command you as I please?

Jane

That would depend on whether you have used your time and experience wisely.

There is a brief silence.

Mr Rochester

Indeed so. I wish I could claim that I had. I am not altogether a villain, Miss Eyre. I might have been as good as you, and wiser. I envy you your peace of mind, your clear conscience... beware remorse, Miss Eyre. Remorse is the poison of life.

Jane

(*Confused*) I don't understand you, sir.

Mr Rochester

Do I alarm you?

Jane

I am bewildered, sir, not afraid.

Adèle enters wearing her new dress. She dances over to Mr Rochester.

Adèle

Monsieur, thank you a thousand times for your kindness. (*She curtsies deeply*) That's what Mamma used to do, isn't it, monsieur?

Mr Rochester

(*Bleakly*) Exactly what your mother used to do. Go and play, Adèle. Vas t'en.

Adèle looks at Mr Rochester uncertainly, then curtsies again and exits.

Mr Rochester

I should not have asked you to become Adèle's governess, Miss Eyre, without knowing her history. You shall know it now.

Jane

I am sure it is not necessary...

Mr Rochester	(*Standing suddenly and speaking forcefully*) I shall judge what is necessary. Adèle's mother was a French opera dancer, Céline Varens. Ugly as I was, I believed that she loved me. I set her up in a hotel, and showered her with gifts. One night, I called for her. She was out, so I waited on the balcony, in perfect happiness, for her to return. And return she did. Below me a carriage drew up. From it stepped Céline, in the company of a young officer: a brainless and vicious youth. Have you ever felt jealousy, Miss Eyre? (*Jane shakes her head*) You astonish me. You sit there quietly as if it were the most usual thing in the world for a man like me to tell you stories of my opera-mistresses; but not so strange perhaps. I think you have a talent for listening.
Jane	Did you leave the balcony, sir?
Mr Rochester	I did not. I drew the curtain, and remained hidden as they came into the room. They began to talk. Shallow, heartless, senseless chatter... my name came up. Céline amused herself by describing what she called my 'deformities'. I opened the window and walked in upon them. I arranged a meeting with the young man at the Bois de Boulogne the following day, and put a bullet through his arm.
Jane	Then Adèle... is your daughter?
Mr Rochester	How can I tell? I never saw Céline Varens again, but some years later I learnt that she had run away to Italy with a singer, leaving behind a daughter. I found Adèle destitute. I brought her here, and Mrs Fairfax found you to... train her. Well now, Miss Eyre, do you regret having accepted the post of governess to the illegitimate child of a French opera girl?
Jane	Adèle is not to blame for her mother's faults, sir... or yours.
Mr Rochester	Even as you fall in with my wishes, you twist a knife in my heart. (*Jane opens her mouth to protest*) No! You are right. I have not always sought goodness, and when I have sought it, I have never found it. Perhaps I have found it now.
	Mr Rochester seems to be about to say something else, but bites back the words. He then speaks abruptly.

| Mr Rochester | Good day, Miss Eyre. |

Mr Rochester exits. Leah enters with a candle, puts it on the table and exits. The lights dim slightly. Jane rises and speaks to the audience.

| Jane | I thought many times about the tale Mr Rochester had told me. I supposed there was, after all, nothing very extraordinary about it. I appreciated his honesty in telling me the truth about Adèle. I became accustomed to his moodiness, his silences, his sudden confidences. Sometimes, it seemed to me that he sought my company. I wondered again why he came so seldom to Thornfield, and whether he would leave again soon. I found I did not wish him to leave again soon. |

From off stage, comes a wordless murmur followed by the same low and horrible laughter heard before. Jane looks around, nervously. She picks up a book and sits down to read.

| Jane | (*To the audience*) One evening, I had sat up late reading; I heard once again the strange laughter that had greeted my arrival, but closer now, and somehow, more frightening. |

The laughter is heard again.

| Jane | (*Calling out*) What is it? Who's there? |

Jane puts down the book, gets up and moves towards the wings, as the sound of laughter is heard again.

| Jane | Is that Mrs Fairfax?... Grace Poole? |

There is more laughter. Smoke begins to billow in from the wings*. Jane stares at it for a moment.

| Jane | Mr Rochester! Adèle! |

She rushes into the smoke and exits. Sound and lighting effects increase the intensity of the fire off stage.

Jane   (*Off stage*) Wake! Wake up, Mr Rochester!

*There is a billow of smoke from the wings and a hiss as if the fire is suddenly extinguished. There is a roar of anger off stage and **Mr Rochester** enters, stumbling. His face, hair and nightshirt are dripping wet. **Jane** enters after him.*

Mr Rochester   What's the matter? Is it a flood?

Jane   Your room was on fire, sir.

Mr Rochester   Is that Jane Eyre? Have you tried to drown me, you witch?

Jane   I heard strange laughter; I tried to find out who it was that laughed so. I saw smoke coming from under your bedroom door. I went in. You were lying in bed, fast asleep, and the bedclothes were on fire.

Mr Rochester   Did you not call out to me?

Jane   I did, sir, but you would not wake, so I took the basin of water from your washstand and flung it over you.

***Mr Rochester** looks at his dripping clothes.*

Mr Rochester   (*Ruefully*) It must have been a full basin.

Jane   Not very full, sir. I had to fling the jug as well. Shall I wake Mrs Fairfax?

Mr Rochester   What on earth for? What can she do? No, sit down here. I shall take this candle and leave you for a moment.

***Jane** sits down. **Mr Rochester** picks up the candle from the table and exits. Off stage, the laughter rings out. **Jane** gets up and moves to follow Mr Rochester.*

*After a brief silence, the laughter is heard again, followed by running footsteps, a scuffle, a moan, then silence again. **Jane** stops suddenly and looks off stage as if she sees someone approaching. She retreats uncertainly to the sofa. To her relief, **Mr Rochester** enters.*

Mr Rochester   I have found it all out. It is as I thought.

Jane   Was it Grace Poole, sir?

Mr Rochester   Grace Poole? What of Grace Poole?

Jane   When I heard the laughter before, Mrs Fairfax said…

Mr Rochester   (*Awkwardly*) Just so. Yes, you have guessed it. I must give some thought to Grace Poole. In the meantime, say nothing of tonight's incident. It is time you went to your own room. The servants will be up soon.

Jane   Goodnight then, sir.

Mr Rochester   What? Are you going, just like that? At least shake hands.

*They do so. There is a pause. **Mr Rochester** does not release **Jane's** hand.*

Mr Rochester   You have saved my life, Jane. I could not bear to be in debt to anyone… except you. I knew you would do me good in some way, the first time I saw you.

Jane   I am glad I happened to be awake.

*There is another pause. **Mr Rochester** still does not release **Jane's** hand. **Jane** starts to tremble.*

Jane   I am cold, sir.

Mr Rochester   Cold – yes. Once more, then, goodnight.

*But still, **Mr Rochester** continues to hold **Jane's** hand. They face each other without speaking, and seem to be about to move closer to each other when **John**, a servant, enters, dressed in his nightclothes. **Mr Rochester** lets go of **Jane's** hand. **John** is surprised at Mr Rochester's wet hair and clothes, but knows his place and quickly puts his face straight.*

Mr Rochester   John? What is it?

John   I beg your pardon sir, has there been some... disturbance?

Mr Rochester   There has been a fire, John. Miss Eyre has put it out.

John   Very good, sir. There's a visitor for Miss Eyre, sir. She says it's urgent.

Mr Rochester   At this hour! Oh very well, show her in.

*John exits. **Mr Rochester** turns to speak to Jane.*

Mr Rochester   Perhaps the faery folk have come for you, after all.

*John enters with **Bessie**, then exits.*

Jane   Bessie? Is it you? Bessie!

***Bessie** is also surprised at Mr Rochester's appearance, but quickly turns her attention to Jane.*

Bessie   Miss Jane... sir... they told me at Lowood you had come here, miss. I followed as quickly as I could...

Jane   But what brings you here at this hour? Is there something amiss with the family?

Bessie   They are very badly at present, miss... in great trouble.

Jane   I hope no one is dead.

Bessie	Mr John died a week ago yesterday, at his chambers in London. It was a very shocking kind of death, miss... they say he killed himself.
Jane	(*To Mr Rochester*) Bessie means my cousin, sir. John Reed.
Bessie	When your aunt heard the news, it brought on a stroke. Lord knows whether she knows what she is saying, but she has been calling for you, miss.
Jane	Then I must go to her. (*To Mr Rochester*) Sir, may I?
Mr Rochester	Promise me only to stay a week...
Jane	I had better not give my word, I may be obliged to break it.
Mr Rochester	But you will come back? (*Jane nods*) Then you and I must say goodbye for a while. How do people perform that ceremony of parting? Teach me.
Jane	They say, farewell, or whatever form they prefer.
Mr Rochester	Then say it.
Jane	Farewell, Mr Rochester, for the present.
Mr Rochester	What must I say?
Jane	The same, sir.
Mr Rochester	Farewell, Miss Eyre, for the present. Is that all?
Jane	Yes.
Mr Rochester	It hardly seems enough. It is blank and cool – farewell.

> *Mr Rochester seizes Jane's hand as if to kiss it. At the last moment, he changes his mind and almost flings her hand away. He turns and exits. Jane stares after him. Bessie stands, open-mouthed in astonishment, as the lights fade.*

• •

Scene 5

*Mrs Reed's bedchamber at Gateshead. The lights come up on the bed. **Mrs Reed**, shrunken and pitiful, is propped up in it. She is unable to move, and to begin with her mind is wandering. **Jane** enters and approaches the bed.*

Mrs Reed   (*Weakly*) Is that Jane Eyre?

Jane   Yes, Aunt Reed.

Mrs Reed   I have had more trouble with that child than anyone would believe. I declare, she talked to me once like something mad... no child ever spoke or looked as she did. Why did she not die in the fever at Lowood? I wish she had died!

There is a pause.

Jane   (*Calmly*) Why do you hate her so?

Mrs Reed   I hated the child the first time I set eyes on it: a sickly, whining, pining thing. My husband pitied it for its mother's sake. He loved his sister's child better than his own; he would try to make my darlings friendly to the little beggar. In his last illness he made me promise to keep the creature... he was weak, weak. John is not like his father. How I wish he would stop tormenting me with letters asking for money. I have no money. He has gambled it all, and lost it, poor boy. He is sunk so low, so low. Who is that?

Jane   It is I, Aunt Reed.

*****Mrs Reed's** mind seems to clear.*

Mrs Reed   I must ease my mind before I die. Is there no one in the room but you?

Jane   No one, aunt.

Mrs Reed   I have twice done you a wrong. One was in breaking the promise I gave my husband to bring you up as my own child...

Jane   And the other?

Mrs Reed	You have another uncle… your father's brother, John Eyre. He is a merchant in the island of Madeira. He wrote to me three years ago saying that he wished to adopt you as his heir. I told him you had died of typhoid fever at Lowood.
Jane	Why?
Mrs Reed	You told me you hated me most of anyone in the world. You said I had treated you with miserable cruelty. You were in a fury; I felt as though an animal I had whipped had looked up at me with human eyes and cursed me in a human voice.
Jane	I was a child then; and it was long ago.
Mrs Reed	Act as you please. Write and tell your uncle I lied, if you will. I think you were born to be my torment, Jane Eyre.
Jane	Love me, or hate me as you will. You have my forgiveness. Ask God for his, and be at peace.

*The light on the bed fades until **Mrs Reed** is in darkness. **Jane** steps away from the bed. The lights rise as **Eliza**, cold and pious, and **Georgina**, plump and self-centred, enter downstage, followed by **Bessie**. **Jane** moves to join them.*

Eliza	(*To Georgina*) Georgina, a more vain and absurd animal than you never walked the earth. You are a fat, weak, puffy, useless thing. When our mother dies, I shall wash my hands of you.
Georgina	(*To Eliza*) Everybody knows, Eliza, that you are the most selfish, heartless creature in existence. You could not bear to see me wife to Lord Edwin, and raised above you, so you ruined my whole life…

***Georgina** sees Jane and stops, her hand to her mouth.*

Georgina	Mamma?
Jane	It is over.
Georgina	Mamma!

She bursts into extravagant sobs and rushes off stage. **Eliza** *crosses herself.*

Eliza   (*To the world in general*) She might have lived to a good age. Her life was shortened by trouble.

She exits the opposite way to that taken by **Georgina.** **Jane** *looks at Bessie for an explanation of* **Georgina** *and* **Eliza's** *behaviour.*

Bessie   A young lord fell in love with Miss Georgina while she was in London. They had decided to run away together, but Miss Eliza found them out and told his relations. They are forever quarrelling now. (*Pause*) She's gone, then? (**Jane** *nods*) She told you about your uncle John?

Jane   She did.

Bessie   I heard her speak of it in her illness. It was much on her mind that she never told you about him. Well, it's all done now. Let me take a proper look at you, Miss Jane.

Bessie *stands with her arms folded and looks at Jane critically.*

Bessie   You've not grown so very tall, nor so very stout.

Jane   I am afraid you are disappointed in me, Bessie.

Bessie   No, Miss Jane, not exactly. You are genteel enough; you look like a lady. It's as much as I ever expected of you – you were no beauty as a child.

Jane *smiles. After a moment, so does* *Bessie.* *They embrace as the lights fade.*

. . . .

Act 3
· · · · · · ·

Scene 1

*Thornfield Hall, as for Act 2. The lights come up on Mr Rochester's guests who are preparing to play charades. **Jane** enters to this scene of confusion. **Lady Lynn** and **Colonel Dent** are busy, crossing and re-crossing the stage, consulting **John** and **Leah**, fetching costume items and 'props' to use during the game that is about to take place. They are too busy to be aware of Jane. **Henry Lynn** enters and calls back off stage.*

Henry Lynn	Fred! Fred! Have you found a bucket for me yet?

Frederick Lynn enters carrying a coal scuttle.

Frederick Lynn	Will this do, Henry?
Henry Lynn	Not a bit of it! Try the stables… and don't forget the brush!

*Henry and Frederick exit in opposite directions. **Lady Ingram** and **Mary Ingram** enter.*

Lady Ingram	Mary, have you succeeded in finding a dress for Blanche?
Mary Ingram	No, mother, she says she will wear her nightdress if she must.
Lady Ingram	In front of… ridiculous! She will have to make do with a veil.

*The guests and the servants exit. **Jane**
watches them go in astonishment. **Mrs**
Fairfax enters carrying a cloak, and **Jane**
seizes her by the arm.*

Jane   Mrs Fairfax!

Mrs Fairfax   Oh, Miss Eyre, back at last, thank goodness. Adèle has been
                           running wild since you left...

Jane   Please, what is going on?

Mrs Fairfax   Charades. Oh dear, let me catch my breath. Mr Rochester's
                           guests have decided to play a game of charades this evening,
                           and everyone is looking for things to wear and so on. I'm quite
                           rushed off my feet.

Jane   But who are these people?

Mrs Fairfax   Friends of Mr Rochester: Lady Lynn and her sons Henry and
                           Frederick; Lady Ingram and her daughters Mary and Blanche;
                           and Colonel Dent. We have had a time of it here, such an
                           airing of rooms and turning of beds you never saw...

                           *She breaks off as **Mr Rochester** enters with
                           Blanche Ingram on his arm, followed by
                           Lady Ingram, **Mary**, **Colonel Dent** and
                           Lady Lynn. **Adèle** enters from the opposite
                           side of the stage; she has obviously dressed
                           with great care.*

Adèle   Mesdames et monsieurs, bonsoir.

Blanche Ingram   Oh, what a little poppet!

Mr Rochester   I see you, at least, are ready for our game, Adèle.

                           ***Adèle** sees **Jane** and rushes to hug her
                           enthusiastically.*

Adèle   Mademoiselle Eyre!

Blanche Ingram	(*Unpleasantly*) Ah, is this the missing governess? You should hear dear Mamma on the question of governesses. Mary and I must have had a dozen at least in our day, each one more ridiculous and detestable than the last… were they not, Mamma?
Lady Ingram	My dearest, don't mention governesses; the word makes me nervous.
Blanche Ingram	Oh, what tricks I used to play on our Miss Wilsons, and Mrs Greys, and Madame Jouberts! Do you remember Madame Joubert, Mary? How she would rage when we spilt our tea and threw our bread and butter across the room, and cry, 'Oh, you villains child!'
Mary Ingram	Poor Madame Joubert.
Blanche Ingram	Nonsense, she deserved it. And Miss Wilson, remember how she took the liberty of falling in love with our brother's tutor, and I found out and told Mamma, and she threw them both out. A detestable race! Enough of governesses, it is time for a new topic, is it not, Mr Rochester?
Mr Rochester	Madam, I support you on this point as on every other.

> *Blanche strikes a dramatic pose; she is showing off. Mr Rochester follows her lead.*

Blanche Ingram	Signor Eduardo, will you sing for us?
Mr Rochester	(*Dramatically*) If you command it, Donna Bianca.
Blanche Ingram	Then let us have a song while we wait for the charade to be prepared. You shall sing the 'Song of the Highwayman'. I adore highwaymen; for that reason, you must sing with passion.
Mr Rochester	I should not dare to displease you.

> *Blanche leads the party out; only Jane and Mrs Fairfax remain. There is the sound of a piano off stage, and Mr Rochester singing. After a moment's silence, Jane speaks to Mrs Fairfax.*

Jane   I did not know Mr Rochester could sing. Miss Ingram plays well, does she not?

Mrs Fairfax   I am no judge of music. Mr Rochester says she does.

Jane   And this beautiful and accomplished lady is not yet married?

Mrs Fairfax   It appears not.

Jane   I wonder no gentleman has taken a fancy to her – Mr Rochester for instance.

Mrs Fairfax   Oh, but he is near forty; she is but twenty-five.

Jane   (*Looking off stage towards the music*) Yet Mr Rochester is evidently much taken with her. Look how she leans her head towards him.

Mrs Fairfax   I daresay he admires her. Oh, dear, here I am chattering away and we shall never be ready for the charade. Excuse me, my dear.

> *Mrs Fairfax exits. **Jane** turns and speaks to the audience. During her speech, the song ends and the guests applaud.*

Jane   I thought of Mr Rochester, and what I had allowed myself to believe his feelings towards me might be. I thought of the beautiful Blanche, and the probability of a marriage between her and Mr Rochester, and I came to this conclusion: that a greater fool than Jane Eyre never breathed. How could I ever have imagined that I was a favourite of Mr Rochester? That I was important to him in any way? I cursed myself for my blind stupidity. But yet, the moment I saw them together, I knew that if Mr Rochester married Blanche Ingram, it might be for family, or rank, or title, but never for love.

> *Adèle enters and approaches Jane.*

Adèle   Mademoiselle Eyre? What is the matter? You are trembling, and your cheeks are red.

Jane   Nothing is wrong with me, Adèle; I am tired from my journey, and it is warm in the hall. I think I shall go to bed.

Adèle	(*Formally*) Monsieur Rochester says he wants you to see the charade, mademoiselle. I am going to be in it, too!
Jane	If you are in the charade, Adèle, then I shall stay.
Adèle	(*Excitedly*) Oh, bien! I must get ready!

> *Adèle rushes off stage as **Mrs Fairfax**, **Lady Lynn**, **Lady Ingram**, **Mary**, and **Colonel Dent** enter. **John** and another servant enter and move the sofa so that the ladies can sit on it and see the area of the stage reserved for the charade, then they exit. **Colonel Dent** notices Jane.*

Colonel Dent	Will you not join us, Miss…?
Lady Ingram	Indeed, no, Colonel; she looks too stupid for a game of this sort.

> *The ladies (except **Jane**) sit down. **Frederick** enters dressed as a clergyman (his costume is made from a bedsheet) holding a Bible. The on-stage audience begin to make guesses.*

Mary Ingram	(*Excitedly*) Vicar!
Lady Lynn	Bible.
Mary Ingram	Church!

> *Frederick holds up his hand for silence, and begins to hum Mendelssohn's 'Wedding March'. **Mr Rochester** and **Blanche** enter dressed as a bride and groom, with **Adèle** dancing before them, scattering flowers from a basket.*

Lady Lynn	Oh, what a love of a child!

> *The charade actors mime a marriage ceremony. The guessing gets more frantic.*

| **Mary Ingram** | Wedding! |

| **Lady Ingram** | Marriage. |

| **Lady Lynn** | Vows. |

| **Colonel Dent** | Ball and chain! |

| **Lady Lynn** | Oh, Colonel! What a thing to say. |

> *Lady Lynn* and *Mary* laugh. *Lady Ingram* looks huffy. *Mr Rochester* indicates Blanche.

| **Colonel Dent** | Bride! |

> *The charade actors bow, the on-stage audience applaud. **Mr Rochester** removes his jacket. **John**, looking long-suffering, enters carrying a bucket with a brush inside and sets it at Mr Rochester's feet. **Henry** enters prancing like a horse. **Mr Rochester** quietens him (as he would a horse) and pretends to brush him down. The guesses come thick and fast.*

| **Mary Ingram** | Horse! |

| **Lady Lynn** | Stable. |

| **Mary Ingram** | Whinny! |

| **Colonel Dent** | No good, Rochester, you'll have to do the whole thing! |

> *Mr Rochester* bows, and puts his jacket back on. The charade actors repeat the first mime, to the confusion of the on-stage audience.

| **Lady Ingram** | But this is just what they did before. |

| **Colonel Dent** | We know this part of the word, Rochester! |

*Then **Blanche** indicates Mr Rochester.*
*Suddenly, **Mary** claps her hands.*

Mary Ingram   I believe I have it! The first part was bride, and then Mr Rochester was a groom in the stable, and the whole word is... bridegroom!

The charade actors bow and the on-stage audience applaud.

Colonel Dent   That was an infamous cheat, Rochester.

Blanche Ingram   Not at all, Colonel, it was very clever. (*She indicates Mr Rochester*) It was all Edward's idea.

Mr Rochester   (*Jokingly*) The lady is bound to support me; she is, after all, my wife. We were married a moment ago in front of all these witnesses.

***Jane** turns her back on the scene.*

Mary Ingram   We shall perform our charade in the library, and Blanche is to play for us.

*The guests exit. **Mrs Fairfax** follows them with **Adèle**. **Mr Rochester** starts to leave and then turns and approaches **Jane**. As they speak, from off stage comes the sound of voices guessing the second charade, punctuated by laughter, applause and short bursts of piano music.*

Mr Rochester   Why did you not come and speak to me earlier?

Jane   I did not wish to disturb you. You seemed engaged, sir.

Mr Rochester   Oh, did I? And where have you been this past month?

Jane   I have been with my aunt, sir, who is dead.

Mr Rochester   So, elf, you have come back to me from another world. (*Pause*) Will you not come and join the game?

Jane   I am tired, sir.

Mr Rochester	And a little depressed, I think. What about? Tell me.
Jane	Nothing – nothing, sir. I am not depressed.
Mr Rochester	Indeed you are, so depressed that a few more words would bring tears to your eyes. Well, for tonight I excuse you, but understand that so long as my visitors stay, I expect you to appear in the drawing room every evening. Now you may see Adèle to bed. Goodnight – my…

> *Mr Rochester turns abruptly and exits. The lights dim. Jane faces the audience and speaks.*

Jane	I had learned to love Mr Rochester. In the weeks that went by, I found that I could not unlove him; although I felt sure he would marry Blanche Ingram.

> *Blackout.*

. . . .

Scene 2

> *Thornfield Hall, as before. The lights come up on **Lady Ingram, Colonel Dent, Lady Lynn** and **Henry** who are wandering about the stage, or pretending to read, etc. They are all bored. **Jane** speaks to the audience.*

Jane	One afternoon, Mr Rochester was called away. In his absence, the company grew bored and restive. Blanche Ingram, after snapping at everyone and scolding Adèle for pestering her, had gone for a walk with her sister and Frederick Lynn.

> *Mary and Frederick burst onto the stage.*

Mary Ingram	(*Excited*) Mamma, you must go and see!
Lady Ingram	Oh? What must I see?
Mary Ingram	The gypsy!

Lady Ingram	What gypsy? Really, Mary, you are tiresome.
Mary Ingram	Freddie and I were walking in the garden with Blanche, and we came across a gypsy woman, a real old crone, sitting beneath the chestnut tree behind the house. Freddie told her to be off, he was terribly brave…
Frederick Lynn	(*Embarrassed*) Well, you know…
Mary Ingram	… but she said she wouldn't stir until the gentry came out to her to have their fortunes told. So I said she might tell my fortune.
Lady Ingram	(*Scandalized*) Mary!
Mary Ingram	Oh, Mamma, she told me such things. She knows all about us!
Lady Ingram	(*Still horrified*) My dear child, what were you thinking of?
Mary Ingram	She knew things we had done when we were children; she described books and ornaments we had at home. And then, she told me she could read my thoughts, and whisper in my ear the name of the gentleman I liked best in all the world.

She looks at Frederick and giggles.

Frederick Lynn	Oh, I say.
Lady Ingram	Gypsies: the very idea! Colonel, Henry, send her about her business at once. I will not have my children associating with such persons.
Mary Ingram	(*Teasing her*) Too late for that, Mamma. Blanche is with her now.
Lady Ingram	(*Faintly*) You left my dearest Blanche alone… unprotected…

> *Lady Ingram breaks off as Blanche enters. Blanche makes a big show of looking unconcerned. She picks up a book, sits on the sofa and pointedly begins to read.*

Mary Ingram	Well, sister? What did she say?

Lady Lynn	How did you feel?
Henry Lynn	Is she a real fortune teller?
Blanche Ingram	(*Disdainfully*) Really, you are all so gullible. I have had my fortune told by a foolish old woman who talked a lot of nonsense, what else would you expect? If I were you, Colonel Dent, I should have her clapped in the stocks without delay.

> *Blanche rises and sweeps off stage, passing* **John** *who enters and approaches* **Jane**. *As the remaining guests murmer to each other about Blanche's strange behaviour,* **John** *whispers a message in* **Jane's** *ear. The guests become quiet as* **Jane** *and* **John** *move downstage. The lights fade on the upstage area. During the following dialogue, Mr Rochester's guests exit and the stage is re-set with a bench and stool. A* **gypsy woman** *enters and sits on the bench.*

Jane	(*To John*) Are you sure she asked for me?
John	Yes, miss. 'I won't see no gentlemen,' that's what she said, 'and I've seen all the ladies; them that's young and single anyway,' she said, 'except for the little one' … beg pardon, miss, that's what she said, 'the governess. You send her to me,' she said.
Jane	Well, I shall see this gypsy, if that is her wish.

> *It is now evening. The lights build slightly on the upstage area to reveal the* **gypsy** *huddled on a bench under a chestnut tree*.* **John** *exits.* **Jane** *approaches the* **gypsy** *who indicates that she should sit down on the stool.* **Jane** *does so and waits patiently for the* **gypsy** *to speak.*

Gypsy	Why don't you tremble?
Jane	I'm not cold.
Gypsy	Why don't you turn pale?

Jane	I'm not sick.
Gypsy	Why don't you ask me your fortune?
Jane	I'm not silly.

*The **gypsy** cackles, then leans forward.*

Gypsy	You are cold; you are sick; you are silly.
Jane	Prove it.
Gypsy	You are cold because you are alone. You are sick at heart. You are silly because you will not reach out and take what you most desire.
Jane	I don't understand riddles.
Gypsy	If you wish me to speak more plainly, show me your palm.
Jane	And I must cross it with silver, I suppose?
Gypsy	To be sure.

***Jane** hands the **gypsy** a shilling. She pockets it.*

Gypsy	(*Dramatically*) I see you sitting in a window seat, observing the company in the house. There is one face you study above all the rest. One you know… and perhaps think well of.
Jane	I don't know the gentlemen here.
Gypsy	No? What of the master of the house? Have you not noticed one lady who always smiles upon Mr Rochester? Who whispers secrets into his ears alone? Have you not looked into the future, and imagined him married, and his bride happy?
Jane	Not exactly. Your witch's skill is rather at fault sometimes.
Gypsy	What the devil have you seen, then?
Jane	I came here to ask questions, not answer them; and to hear my fortune.

Gypsy	Your fortune is doubtful. You may have everything you have ever wished for. Will you not stretch out your hand for it?
Jane	I don't understand you.
Gypsy	Kneel! (*Jane does so*) I see eyes that once shone, made dull by sadness. A mouth made to speak much and smile often, now silent. I see beyond, to a mind strong enough to withstand fire and earthquake.

> *The **gypsy's** voice begins to change until it becomes the voice of Mr Rochester.*

Gypsy	My plans are made, whatever conscience or reason may argue. I have kept myself in check so far; but to do so further is beyond my strength. Rise, Miss Eyre. 'Off, ye lendings.'

> *Mr Rochester stands and tears off his gypsy disguise. **Jane** gets up from her knees and stares at him, shocked. The sound of a wind beginning to blow is heard. During the following dialogue, we hear the storm gathering strength.*

Mr Rochester	(*Amused*) Well, Jane, do you know me?
Jane	(*Recovering from her shock*) Was it fair, sir, to trap me into talking nonsense?
Mr Rochester	Oh, you have been very careful, very sensible. Do you forgive me?
Jane	It is not for me to condemn, or forgive. Miss Ingram seemed very displeased by what you had to tell her.
Mr Rochester	(*Thoughtfully*) Ah, yes, Blanche, my rare beauty. Tell me, faery as you are, can you cast a spell to make me as handsome as she is beautiful?
Jane	It would be beyond the power of magic, sir.
Mr Rochester	A pity. Tell me, Jane, what will you do when I am married?
Jane	I suppose I must leave Thornfield, sir.

Mr Rochester	Yes, I believe you must.
Jane	Then you are to be married, sir?
Mr Rochester	Oh, indeed. Adèle must go to school, and you to a new situation. I believe I have found just the thing: you shall be governess to the five daughters of Mrs Dionysius O'Gall of Bitternutt Lodge, Connaught. You'll like Ireland, I think. The people are very friendly, they say.
Jane	It is such a long way off… from England, and Thornfield… and…
Mr Rochester	And?
Jane	…and you, sir.

She begins to cry.

Mr Rochester	It is a long way indeed. And when you get to Bitternutt Lodge, Connaught, Ireland, I shall never see you again. But no matter; you'll soon forget me.
Jane	That I never should! Oh God… I wish I had never come to Thornfield!
Mr Rochester	Shall you be so sorry to leave Thornfield? Then stay.
Jane	(*Passionately*) I cannot! Do you think I could stay, to become nothing to you? Do you think I have no feelings? That because I am poor, and plain, and little, I have no soul and no heart? You think wrong! Before God, I am your equal.
Mr Rochester	My equal! So, Jane!

He kisses her.

Jane	Let me go! Your bride stands between us.
Mr Rochester	My bride is here; because my equal is here. Jane, will you marry me?

Jane stares at him. She cannot believe what she has heard.

Mr Rochester	Do you doubt me, Jane?
Jane	(*Shocked*) Entirely!
Mr Rochester	You have no faith in me?
Jane	None at all! What about Blanche Ingram?
Mr Rochester	What of her? What love have I for her? None. What love has she for me? None – as I have proved. The gypsy told her just now that my fortune was not a third what she supposed. You saw the result. She and her mother will find some excuse to leave this house tomorrow morning.
Jane	Then why did you go to such trouble to make me believe you wished to marry Miss Ingram?
Mr Rochester	I pretended courtship to Miss Ingram to make you as madly in love with me as I was with you. I knew jealousy would be my strongest weapon in the attempt.
Jane	(*Sarcastically*) Excellent! Now you are as small as the end of my little finger. Did you think nothing of Miss Ingram's feelings?
Mr Rochester	She has no feelings except pride. Was my behaviour so dreadfully wrong?
Jane	It was a scandalous disgrace. Let me look at your face. Turn to the moonlight.
Mr Rochester	Why?
Jane	Because I want to look into your eyes. Do you truly love me, and wish me to be your wife?
Mr Rochester	Jane, poor, and plain, and little as you are; rude, and cross, and ugly as I am, I beg you to accept me as your husband.
Jane	I will.

Mr Rochester holds Jane fiercely to him. He raises his head and cries heavenwards, above the noise of the gathering storm.

Mr Rochester	Then God pardon me, and let no man come between us!

There is a flash of lightning and a deafening peal of thunder, followed by a crash.

Mr Rochester	Look out!

*Both **Mr Rochester** and **Jane** fall to the ground. They are lit by a spotlight. **Mr Rochester** helps **Jane** to her knees.*

Mr Rochester	Are you all right? The lightning… that was too close.
Jane	(*Staring upstage*) Look… the tree.
Mr Rochester	What?
Jane	The old chestnut tree. The lightning struck it. Half of it has split away.

She turns to Mr Rochester. He takes her in his arms as the lights fade to blackout.

Scene 3

*The lights come up on Thornfield Hall, as before. **Mrs Fairfax** enters; she is worried. **John** enters and she stops him as he crosses the stage.*

Mrs Fairfax   John, is the carriage ready?

John   Yes, ma'am. It has been ready for an hour.

Mrs Fairfax   And is everyone ready? We must all be here to greet the master... after... after...

John   (*Interrupting*) Everyone is ready. Leah is seeing to Miss Adèle.

Mrs Fairfax   Has Mr Rochester returned? I do think he should have stayed here last night...

John   Mr Rochester will be here in good time, ma'am. After all, he's not going to miss his own wedding, is he?

John's words do not reassure Mrs Fairfax.

Mrs Fairfax   Wedding... oh, my.

*John gives her an exasperated look, and exits. **Mrs Fairfax** exits too. Jane enters, wearing her wedding dress, and carrying a box. She sits on the sofa, opens the box and places the lid so that the audience cannot see inside. She examines the contents, but puts the lid back on and sets the box aside hurriedly as **Mrs Fairfax** enters. On seeing Jane, **Mrs Fairfax** becomes agitated.*

Mrs Fairfax   Oh, good... good morning, Miss Eyre, that is... oh, dear.

Jane   Dear Mrs Fairfax, it pains me that you are so troubled that Mr Rochester and I are to be married.

Mrs Fairfax sits abruptly, perched on the edge of the sofa. She takes out a small handkerchief and dabs at her eyes.

Mrs Fairfax	I'm sure I don't know how it will turn out; I hope it will all be right in the end. Gentlemen of Mr Rochester's station are not accustomed to marry their governesses. And the difference in ages: he might almost be your father. Is it really for love he is going to marry you?
Jane	Do you think it impossible that he should?
Mrs Fairfax	Oh no, but I fear you may find something different from what you expect.

> *Mr Rochester's voice can be heard off stage. On hearing it, **Mrs Fairfax** starts guiltily and exits hurriedly. **Jane** rises from the sofa.*

Mr Rochester	(*Off stage*) John, take my horse! Mrs Fairfax! Is everybody asleep?

> *Mr Rochester enters. **Jane** rushes across and clings to him.*

Mr Rochester	There! You can't do without me, that's plain. Why, what is it? Is there anything wrong?

> *Jane releases her grip on Mr Rochester.*

Jane	Nothing now; I am neither afraid nor unhappy.
Mr Rochester	But you have been both, my angel.
Jane	Do you wonder at that?
Mr Rochester	The past month you have been as slippery as an eel and as prickly as a thorn bush, and now I seem to have gathered up a stray lamb in my arms. Have you missed your shepherd?
Jane	Yes, I wanted you, but don't boast. It's a careless shepherd that leaves his sheep unattended when there are wolves on the prowl.
Mr Rochester	(*Suddenly attentive*) Wolves, Jane?
Jane	One wolf, at least. You were away from home last night…

Mr Rochester	I told you I had one last piece of business before we left England together… but go on.
Jane	All day yesterday, I was very busy. I packed our cases, and labelled them. I thought how strange it was to be writing 'Mrs Rochester' for that person doesn't yet exist…
Mr Rochester	(*Taking Jane in his arms*) She will exist before noon today.
Jane	(*Breaking away from Mr Rochester*) No, sir, don't touch me now; let me talk undisturbed. In the evening, Leah called me upstairs to look at my wedding dress which had just been delivered. Under it, in the box, I found your present: the veil, covered in jewels and pearls, that you had sent for from London. I suppose you were determined to dress your plain bride as if she were a princess.
Mr Rochester	You would have no jewels or fine clothes from me, what was I to do?
Jane	It scarcely matters, since I cannot wear it now.
	Jane moves to fetch the box from the sofa. She opens it and takes out the wedding veil. It is badly torn. During the following dialogue, the lights dim so that only Jane and Mr Rochester are lit.
Mr Rochester	How has this come about?
Jane	I had a dream last night, sir. I dreamt that Thornfield Hall was a dreary ruin, the home of bats and owls. I heard a horse in the distance, and climbed the ruined walls. You were a speck, riding away from me on a distant road. The wall beneath me crumbled; I fell and woke.
Mr Rochester	And is that all?
Jane	No, as I awoke I was dazzled by the light of a candle.
	*The figure of an **intruder** enters carrying a candle. Her wild hair hides her face.*

Jane	I thought Leah had come in. I heard a rustling from the closet where I had hung my clothes ready for this morning. I felt my blood run cold. Someone was looking at my wedding dress.
Mr Rochester	Then it must have been Leah... or Mrs Fairfax.
Jane	Neither, sir. Nor even Grace Poole. It seemed to be a woman, tall and large, with thick dark hair.

> *The **intruder** approaches Jane, puts down the candle, and takes the veil from her. She mimes to **Jane**'s narration, keeping her back to the audience but her face to Jane.*

Jane	She held up my veil and gazed at it. Then she put it on, and turned to the mirror, and I saw her face.
Mr Rochester	Describe it.
Jane	Fearful and ghastly, discoloured and savage with swollen, dark lips – scarcely human.
Mr Rochester	What did this creature do?

> *The **intruder** continues to mime to **Jane**'s narration. She 'tears' the veil, then picks up the candle and approaches Jane.*

Jane	It ripped my veil from its head and tore it in half. Then it turned, and came towards me until it leant over my bed, holding the candle close to my face.

> *The **intruder** drops the veil into **Jane**'s hands and exits. The lights come up again.*

Jane	I remember nothing more. I must have fainted.
Mr Rochester	Another dream, Jane?

> *Jane passes the veil to **Mr Rochester**.*

Jane	You hold in your own hands, sir, the evidence that it was not.

*Mr Rochester throws aside the veil and clings to **Jane**.*

Mr Rochester Thank God it was only the veil that was harmed. Oh, to think of what might have happened. Jane, you must trust me now. I want no further delay. We shall go straight to the church.

Jane What was it, sir? What is happening?

Mr Rochester What is happening is that we shall be married, and away from this house, before noon. You shall be safe, and no one shall part us. Now, Jane! Now!

*The lights dim upstage. **Mr Rochester** moves into the shadows. **Jane** steps forward to speak to the audience. While she speaks, the torn veil is removed and the stage is re-set with a plain church altar. **Mr Rochester** stands before it. **Mr Wood**, the clergyman, enters and takes up his position. **Richard Mason** and **Mr Briggs** enter and stand to one side.*

Jane Mr Rochester took my hand in a grip of iron, and hurried me along with a stride I could hardly follow – out of the house, down the lane to the church. He seemed possessed by an unshakable purpose. Did any bridegroom ever look as he did? I scarcely heard the words as the service began.

*The lights build to reveal the wedding party. **Jane** moves to Mr Rochester's side as the wedding service continues.*

Mr Wood I require and charge you both, as ye will answer at the dreadful day of judgement when the secrets of all hearts shall be disclosed, that if either of you know any impediment why ye may not lawfully be joined together in matrimony, ye now confess it.

Mr Wood pauses, then makes to continue.

Mr Wood	Wilt thou, Edward Fairfax Rochester, have this woman to thy wedded wife…
Mr Briggs	(*Interrupting*) The marriage cannot go on: I declare the existence of an impediment.
Mr Rochester	(*Forcefully*) Proceed. (**Mr Wood** *hesitates*) Proceed, damn you.
Mr Wood	I cannot proceed. (*To Mr Briggs*) What is the nature of the impediment?
Mr Briggs	It is a quite simple one. Mr Rochester is already married. He has a wife, still living!
Mr Rochester	(*Furiously to Mr Briggs*) Who are you?
Mr Briggs	My name is Briggs. I am a solicitor.
Mr Rochester	And my wife, who is she?
Mr Briggs	She is Bertha Antoinetta Mason, daughter of Jonas Mason, of Spanish Town, Jamaica.
Mr Rochester	You will produce proof of that – or go to hell!
Mr Briggs	My proof is here. Mr Mason, have the goodness to step forward.

> **Mr Rochester** *sees Richard Mason for the first time, and takes one step towards him.*
> **Richard Mason** *ducks behind Mr Briggs.*

Richard Mason	(*Frightened*) My God – don't let him hurt me.
Mr Rochester	Well, Richard, what have you to say?
Richard Mason	My sister is married to this man. She is now living at Thornfield Hall.
Mr Wood	Impossible! I have lived here for years, and I have never heard of a Mrs Rochester at Thornfield Hall.

Mr Rochester	No, by God! I took care that no one should. Enough! Close your book, Wood. There will be no wedding today. What they say is true. I have under my roof Bertha Mason, sister to (*pointing at Richard Mason*) this miserable worm. I married her fifteen years ago, and have kept her for many years in confinement at Thornfield Hall.
Mr Wood	How? Confinement…?
Mr Rochester	Bertha Mason is mad. She came of a mad family: idiots and maniacs through three generations! Briggs, Wood, Mason: I invite you all to come up to the house and visit Grace Poole's patient and my wife!

> *The lights dim until only **Jane** and **Mr Rochester** are lit. They step forward. As they speak, the upstage area is re-set as Bertha Mason's attic prison – bare except for a chair. **Grace Poole** and **Bertha Mason** enter, and take up their positions. **Mr Wood**, **Mr Briggs** and **Richard Mason** stand slightly to one side, in the shadows.*

Jane	(*To the audience*) Still holding me fast, Mr Rochester left the church. At the front door of the hall, we found the carriage.
Mr Rochester	(*Speaking as though to John*) Take it back to the coach-house, John. It will not be needed today.
Jane	(*To the audience*) At the entrance, Mrs Fairfax, Adèle, and Leah were waiting to greet us.
Mr Rochester	(*Speaking as though to the servants*) Away with your congratulations! Who wants them? They are fifteen years too late!
Jane	(*To the audience*) We ascended the stairs, to the third storey. Mr Rochester lifted a tapestry to reveal a concealed door. He unlocked it.

> *The lights build upstage to reveal **Grace Poole** drinking from a bottle which she hides, quickly. **Bertha Mason** is huddled in a corner. She is the intruder who ripped Jane's*

veil. **Mr Rochester** *leads* **Jane,** **Mr Wood,** **Mr Briggs,** *and* **Richard Mason** *into the attic prison.*

Mr Rochester   How are you, Mrs Poole? And how is your patient today?

Grace Poole   We're tolerable, sir. Rather snappish but not 'rageous.

                     Bertha Mason *rises and howls at Mr Rochester.*

Grace Poole   Ah! She sees you, sir. For God's sake, take care.

                     Bertha Mason *flings herself at* **Mr Rochester** *and grapples with him, growling like an animal. Between them,* **Mr Rochester** *and* **Grace Poole** *succeed in forcing her onto a chair and subduing her. During the following dialogue she rocks and moans, darting evil glances at Mr Rochester and Richard Mason.*

Mr Rochester   Gentlemen, this is my wife. You have just seen an example of the only loving embraces I have ever had from her.

Richard Mason   We had better leave her.

Mr Rochester   (*To Richard Mason*) Go to the devil! (*To Mr Briggs*) Has Mr Mason told you the truth about my marriage, Briggs? My father learnt that Jonas Mason would settle thirty thousand pounds on his daughter. He sent me out to Jamaica. Oh, Bertha Mason was a beauty then: tall, dark, majestic, admired by every man in Spanish Town. Her family paraded her before me at parties, splendidly dressed; I was never allowed to see her alone. Before I knew where I was, I was married. Only then did I discover the truth, that her mother was shut in a lunatic asylum; that my wife, too, was sinking rapidly into madness. She was violent, unspeakably coarse, addicted to all manner of vile depravity. And so, for fifteen years of torment, I have kept her close and secret. (*He points at Jane*) At last, this young girl came to me. I saw my best, and last chance for happiness, and I would have taken it. Now judge me, priest of the gospel and man of the law, and remember that you shall yourselves be judged.

Mr Briggs	Miss Eyre, your uncle will be glad to hear of your escape.
Jane	My uncle?
Mr Briggs	John Eyre, of Madeira. You wrote to him that you intended to marry Mr Rochester. By chance, Mr Mason happened to be in Madeira. Knowing his acquaintance with Mr Rochester, your uncle mentioned the matter to him and discovered the truth. Being too sick to travel, your uncle sent Mr Mason to prevent your marriage. I am thankful that we were in time to do so, as I'm sure you must be.

> *Jane gives Mr Briggs a look so full of scorn for his lack of understanding that he coughs and moves to talk to Richard Mason and Mr Wood. **Jane** turns to Mr Rochester. They speak in low voices, unheard by the others.*

Jane	Then it was she who tried to burn you in your bed…
Mr Rochester	And who tore your veil last night. My wife… a foul and murderous demon!
Jane	Do you hate her so much? She cannot help being mad.
Mr Rochester	It is not because she is mad that I hate her. If you were mad, do you think that I should hate you?
Jane	I do.
Mr Rochester	Then you know nothing about me. If your mind were broken, you should be my treasure still, but she… Am I a scoundrel, Jane?
Jane	(*Shaking her head*) I pity you, sir. I do pity you.
Mr Rochester	Then come with me. We shall go away, to Europe, and live as man and wife. I shall not let us be parted.
Jane	I cannot, sir. I love you more than ever, but I must leave you.
Mr Rochester	Jane, don't leave me. It would not be wicked to love me.
Jane	It would be to obey you.

Mr Rochester	(*Threatening*) You shall come with me. Beware of me, Jane, I am not a gentle man.
Jane	Oh, God help me!

*Jane bursts into frenzied weeping. **Mr Rochester** tries to embrace her. **Richard Mason** steps uncertainly toward them. Then, with a howl, **Bertha Mason** breaks away from **Grace Poole**.*

Grace Poole	Look out, sir!

*Bertha Mason buries her teeth into **Richard Mason's** throat. He screams. **Mr Rochester** and **Grace Poole** drag **Bertha Mason** away from Richard Mason. **Mr Briggs** and **Mr Wood** step forward to help the injured man. During the confusion, **Jane** exits quietly.*

Richard Mason	(*Frantic*) Oh God... she's done for me!
Mr Rochester	Nonsense, man; you've lost a little blood, that's all.
Richard Mason	She bit me! She sucked my blood!
Mr Rochester	Hush, now. Wood, get some bandages; Jane, fetch some water...

Mr Rochester looks round for Jane and realizes that she has disappeared.

Mr Rochester	Where is she? Gone? Find her! Jane! Jane!

*The lights fade until only **Mr Rochester** is lit.*

Mr Rochester	Jane!

The lights fade to blackout.

• •

Act 4
· · · · · · ·

Scene 1

*The parlour at Marsh End. The stage is set with plain furniture, including a couple of fireside chairs. It is late in the evening and the sound of a storm can be heard. The lights come up on **Mary** and **Diana Rivers** who are occupied in household tasks. Their servant, **Hannah**, is clearing things away. From off stage, there is a crash of a door being flung open, and the sound of the storm gets louder. **St John Rivers** enters, carrying the bedraggled body of **Jane Eyre** in his arms. **Mary** and **Diana** immediately help him to carry her to a chair.*

Hannah   Why, what have you got there, Mr St John? I declare, it's that beggar woman that came round earlier. I sent her about her business... there are bad folk about, housebreakers and such...

St John   Hush, Hannah. It was your duty to keep her out; it's mine to let her in.

Mary   St John, who is it?

St John   I cannot tell; I found her collapsed at our door.

Mary   She is worn to nothing.

St John   Mary, bring the smelling-salts. Hannah, some milk and a piece of bread.

Mary and Hannah exit.

Diana   Is she ill, or only hungry?

St John   Hungry, I think. Let us see.

*Hannah returns with bread and milk, followed by **Mary** carrying a small bottle which she gives to **St John**. He waves it*

*under **Jane's** nose and she coughs and*
*awakes. **Diana** takes the bread and milk*
from Hannah.

Diana   (*To Jane*) Try to eat.

*Diana feeds **Jane**, who eats a little.*

St John   Not too much at first, Diana. (*To Jane*) What is your name?

Jane   My name is Jane Elliot.

St John   And where do you live? Where are your friends?

Jane says nothing.

St John   Can we send for anyone you know?

Jane says nothing.

St John   What account can you give of yourself?

Jane   Sir, I can give you no details tonight.

Diana   Then what can we do for you?

Jane   Do with me and for me as you will... I...

She faints.

St John   Fetch a blanket, Mary.

Mary exits and returns with a blanket
which she tucks around Jane.

Diana   (*To St John*) She is very weak. It is very well you brought her
                   in.

St John   Yes, she would certainly have been found dead at our door in
                   the morning if I had not.

Diana   (*Indicating the smelling-salts in St John's hand*) Will you revive
                   her again?

St John	No. She is asleep now; that will do her more good than anything else we could devise.
Mary	I wonder what she has gone through?
St John	Strange hardships, I imagine.
Mary	She is something more than a poor beggar. She has an unusual face.
St John	Rather a plain face; sensible, but not at all handsome.
Diana	She is so ill, St John.
St John	Ill or well, she would always be plain.

> *The lights dim.* **St John**, **Mary**, **Diana**, *and* **Hannah** *exit. The sound of birdsong fills the stage and the lights brighten. It is a sunny morning.* **Jane** *slowly awakes and speaks to the audience.*

Jane	I lay for four days between sleep and waking. I discovered that my rescuer was a clergyman, St John Rivers, and my nurses were Mary and Diana, his sisters. They were very kind to me, though their servant, Hannah, continued to view me with suspicion.

> **Hannah** *enters and busies herself with polishing some brassware.* **Jane** *turns and watches her.*

Hannah	(*Noticing Jane*) You shouldn't be out of bed yet.

> **Jane** *gets up from the chair. She is still rather weak.*

Jane	I am much better. Let me help you with the polishing.
Hannah	Nay, I don't want ye to do naught.
Jane	I must do something.

Jane takes a brass ornament and begins to polish it. There is a pause.

Hannah	Did you ever go a-begging afore you came here?
Jane	I am no more a beggar than yourself or your young ladies.
Hannah	I dunnut understand that. You've no house, nor no brass, I guess?
Jane	Lack of those things does not make me a beggar.
Hannah	Humph! Are you book-learned?
Jane	I was at a boarding school eight years.
Hannah	Why ever can't ye keep yourself, then?
Jane	I have kept myself, and will do so again.

Jane holds out the ornament to Hannah for inspection.

Hannah	Ye're no servant; I see by your hands.
Jane	Never mind what I have been. Tell me the name of this house.
Hannah	This is Marsh End.
Jane	Have you been with the family long?
Hannah	Thirty year.
Jane	Then you must be an honest and faithful servant; though you were unkind enough to call me a beggar…
Hannah	Aye, well, there's any number of cheats about…
Jane	…and turned me from your door, on a night when you would not have shut out a dog.
Hannah	(*Embarrassed*) You musn't think too hardly of me. I reckon I were wrong about you. You look a right down decent little creature.

Jane	Then I forgive you. Shake hands.

> *Seriously, they shake hands, as **Mary** and **Diana** enter.*

Mary	(*To Jane*) Well now! What are you doing out of bed?
Diana	And what are you doing there? (*She indicates the ornaments*) You are a visitor.
Mary	Come, leave that. Sit down here, while Hannah gets the tea ready.

> ***Hannah** exits as **St John** enters.*

Diana	St John, look – Miss Elliot is feeling better.

> ***Jane** is startled. She has forgotten that she gave a false name. **St John** notices her reaction.*

St John	You said your name was Jane Elliot?
Jane	I did say so. It is the name by which I wish to be called at present, though it is not my true name.
St John	Will you tell us where you have come from?
Jane	I cannot tell you that.
St John	Then how can we write to your friends to say that you are safe?
Jane	I have no home, and no friends.
St John	And you have never been married?
Diana	Why, St John, she can't be above seventeen or eighteen years old.
Jane	I am nineteen, but I am not married. No.
Mary	You are too inquisitive, St John.

St John	Miss… Elliot, if I know nothing about you, I cannot help you. And you need help, do you not? How did you come here?

*The lights dim leaving **St John**, **Mary** and **Diana** in the shadows. **Jane** steps forward to speak to the audience.*

Jane	And so I told St John and his sisters of my wanderings, which had at last brought me to their door. Of the desolate moor where the coachman had set me down, saying he could take me no further for the fare I had given him. Of nights sleeping on the damp heather, with nothing to eat but wild bilberries; days of walking, faint with hunger, with no money, no food, and no hope.

*A **woman** enters with a basket of bread. **Jane** stops her.*

Jane	Please, I am a stranger here, looking for work. Is there a dressmaker in the village?
Woman	(*Eyeing Jane suspiciously*) Two or three. We don't need any more.
Jane	Then is there any place nearby where a servant is wanted?
Woman	Nay, I couldn't say.
Jane	What do people do here?
Woman	Farm work, mostly, or working at Mr Oliver's needle factory. But he don't employ women.
Jane	Then what do women do?
Woman	I knaw not. Some does one thing and some another. Poor folk must get on as they can.
Jane	(*Offering a handkerchief*) Would you give me some bread for this handkerchief?
Woman	Nay. What could I do with it?

*The **woman** sniffs scornfully and exits.
Jane turns back to the audience.*

Jane   I had left the moors, and spent the night in a wood. It was
                cold; it rained that night, and all the next day. By evening, I
                was starving. I begged a mess of cold porridge from a woman
                who was about to feed it to her pig.

*The lights build to reveal **St John**, **Mary**
and **Diana**. **Jane** turns back to them.*

Jane   (*To St John*) Soon afterwards, I saw the light from your
                window. I felt I would rather die near a warm hearth that on
                the road, or in a field. And here I have met with true kindness
                and generosity.

St John   Yet you would not wish, I am sure, to depend on our
                generosity for longer than necessary.

Diana   (*Shocked*) St John! (*To Jane, kindly*) Miss Elliot, you shall stay
                here for as long as you like.

Mary   Indeed, you shall.

St John   My sisters, you see, have a pleasure in keeping you; as if you
                were a half-frozen bird found lying in the snow. I feel more
                inclined to find you the means of keeping yourself.

Diana   She has already said that she is willing to do anything honest
                she can do.

Jane   I will be a dressmaker, a servant, or anything you will.

St John   Then I shall aid you; in my own time, and in my own way.

*St **John** exits. During the following speech,
Jane comes downstage and **Diana** exits and
returns with a piece of card and a pencil.*

Jane   (*To the audience*) The more I knew of the Rivers, the better I
                liked them. Diana's high spirits inspired me, Mary's calmness
                soothed me. Only with St John did I feel no bond of affection.
                He was, without doubt, a good man: strong in his faith, tireless
                in his duties. But he was not lovable.

Jane rejoins the sisters. *Diana* hands her the
piece of card and the pencil. *Jane* sits and
begins to sketch Mary. All three are in
giggling high spirits. *St John* enters reading
a letter. *Mary* waves to him.

Mary   Well? Is it a good likeness?

Jane   You must keep still.

Diana looks at the drawing over *Jane's*
shoulder.

Diana   Not a good likeness at all. You've made her a great deal too
              handsome. Look, St John.

Mary   Oh, let me see.

Diana   You shan't see until it's finished.

Mary gets up and tries to see the picture.
Diana tries to prevent her.

Mary   St John, tell her to let me see the picture…

She falters when she realizes from St John's
silence that there is something wrong.

Diana   St John? What is wrong?

St John   Our uncle John is dead.

Diana   Dead?

St John   Yes.

Diana   And what then?

St John   Why, nothing. Read.

He passes the letter to **Diana**. *Mary* moves
to read it over her shoulder. *Jane* looks from
them to St John.

St John	Miss Elliot, you will think us hard-hearted, but we have never met our uncle. My father and he quarrelled long ago. Uncle John made a great fortune, I believe, some twenty thousand pounds. He was never married and had only one other living relation, no more closely related to him than we.
Diana	(*Putting the letter down*) At any rate, it leaves us no worse off than we were before.

> **Diana** *is close to tears.* **Mary** *leads her from the stage.*

St John	The cause of the quarrel was that my uncle had given my father bad advice about investments, which ruined him. He hoped that Uncle John would leave his possessions to us to make up, but he has chosen to leave everything to the other relation. Had he left us even a small part of his fortune, my sisters and I could have continued to live together. Now, we must part.
Jane	What will they do? What will you do?
St John	My course is already set out before me. As for Mary and Diana, they shall go to work as governesses.
Jane	And what shall I do? Have you found employment for me?
St John	Nothing grand or enviable. Some might think it degrading. When I came here, the village had no school. I began one for the boys and now I mean to open one for the girls. Will you be its teacher?
Jane	I will, with all my heart.
St John	You do understand? It is a village school; your pupils will be poor girls. You will do well to teach them to read and write. Do you know what you undertake?
Jane	I do.
St John	Then so be it.

> *He kisses her, but formally, as a priest gives a kiss as a blessing. The lights fade.*

Scene 2

*Morton School. The stage is set with rough benches, slates and a chalkboard. The lights come up on **Jane** who is cleaning the chalkboard. She looks up as **St John** enters, carrying a parcel.*

Jane   Mr Rivers. Please come in. Would you like some tea?

St John   No, I cannot stay. My sisters asked me to give you this.

*He passes a parcel to **Jane**. She opens it.*

Jane   A paint box, and pencils and paper. That is kind of Diana and Mary.

St John looks at Jane closely.

St John   Have you found your first day's work harder than expected?

Jane   Oh no! I think in time I shall get on with my pupils very well.

St John   Your cottage – the furniture – are scanty indeed…

Jane   A few weeks ago I had nothing. I was a homeless vagrant. Now I have friends, a home, and work to do.

***Rosamond Oliver**, a well-dressed, pretty and charming girl, enters, unseen by **St John** and **Jane**.*

St John   I hope you do indeed feel as contented as you say you do. Nevertheless…

Rosamond	(*Interrupting*) Good evening, Mr Rivers. You are quite a stranger.

> *St John's back is turned towards Rosamond. His reaction to her voice is one of pain rather than pleasure.*

St John	Miss Oliver. It is a lovely evening, but late for you to be out alone.

> *Rosamond joins St John and Jane.*

Rosamond	I only returned home this afternoon. Papa told me you had opened your school... is this the new teacher?
St John	It is. (*He introduces them*) Miss Elliot: Miss Rosamond Oliver. It is by her father's gift that I have been able to open this school.
Jane	Your father owns the factory in the valley?
Rosamond	He makes needles. He says it is because he has a sharp business sense. That's his favourite joke; indeed, it is his only joke. I am pleased to meet you, Miss Elliot. (*She shakes hands with Jane*) Do you think you shall like Morton?
Jane	I hope I shall.
Rosamond	Are your pupils attentive?
Jane	Quite.
Rosamond	Do you like your house? Have I furnished it nicely?
Jane	I do, and you have; very nicely indeed.
Rosamond	I shall come up and help you teach sometimes. It will be a change for me to visit you now and then, and I like a change. Oh, Mr Rivers, I wish you had been able to join our party. We danced until two o'clock this morning, and the officers of the light cavalry were there, such gallant men and so charming.

> *St John frowns at her. Rosamond laughs at him and turns to Jane.*

Rosamond	Mr Rivers is a terrible puritan. You must come and visit us at the hall, Miss Elliot. Papa would very much like to meet you. He says that Mr Rivers never comes to see us now. (*To St John, more seriously*) He is alone this evening and not very well. Will you return with me and visit him?
St John	It is too late to intrude on Mr Oliver.
Rosamond	It is not too late at all! This is just the time when Father wants company; when the works are closed and he has no business to occupy him. I know that Mary and Diana left today, so I am sure you must be lonely. Do come.
St John	(*With an effort*) Not tonight, Miss Rosamond, not tonight.
Rosamond	(*Disappointed*) Well, if you are so obstinate, I will leave you. Good evening. Miss Elliot. Mr Rivers.
Jane	Good evening.
St John	Good evening.

> *Rosamond starts to leave. She pauses and turns as if she is about to say something more, but St John's stern look stops her. She exits.*

Jane	Diana once told me that you were a good brother and a gentle man, but in some things, as hard as flint. I begin to see what she meant.
St John	A year ago, I heard a call from heaven to rise up and do God's bidding. He had an errand for me: to become a missionary. I shall soon leave England forever to do the Lord's work in distant lands.
Jane	Do Diana and Mary approve of your decision?
St John	They know that it is right. When I have found a successor for my parish, there remains only one last conflict with human weakness to overcome; and I shall leave for the East.
Jane	You are hard to dismiss Miss Rosamond Oliver as a mere human weakness.

St John	My heart is no longer mine to give. I have laid it on a sacred altar. Soon, holy fires will consume it.
Jane	And is there no room in your heart for Miss Oliver?

> *St John leaves abruptly. Jane turns and speaks to the audience.*

Jane	St John Rivers was a frequent visitor to my little school. It seemed to me that he approved of the progress that I was making with my pupils. Rosamond Oliver also came often: always lively, always graceful. I saw that, though St John would have given the world for her, he would not sacrifice one chance of heaven for her sake; and I felt pity for them both. Months passed. In the face of St John's indifference, Miss Oliver's visits became less frequent, and finally stopped altogether.

> *Jane picks up her paper, brush and paints and begins work.*

Jane	One day, when the pupils had a holiday, I was colouring in an old sketch of Rosamond Oliver when St John came visiting.

> *St John enters.*

St John	What have you there? Let me see.

> *St John becomes very still as he examines the drawing. Then he sets it aside casually.*

Jane	Is the portrait a good likeness?
St John	Of whom? I did not observe it closely.
Jane	You did, Mr Rivers. Would you like to have this picture? Would it comfort you to have a picture of Miss Oliver, when you are far away?
St John	I should certainly like to have it, but it would not be wise.
Jane	Not wise?

St John	(*Calmly*) Rosamond Oliver is about to be married to a Mr Granby, the son of Sir Frederick Granby.
Jane	(*After a pause*) They cannot have known one another long.
St John	Two months. You see, Jane, the battle is fought and the victory won.
Jane	Victory can come at too great a cost.
St John	Not in this case. My way is now clear; I thank God for it. Now, I have a story to tell you. Leave your work for a moment and attend to me.

St John waits until Jane has cleared away her art materials. They both sit down.

St John	Twenty years ago, a poor clergyman fell in love with a rich man's daughter. Her family disowned the couple immediately after the wedding. Before two years had passed, both were dead, leaving a daughter to be brought up by an aunt – a Mrs Reed, of Gateshead. (*Jane starts*) Did you hear a noise?
Jane	(*Recovering herself*) No.
St John	Well, to continue: at ten years old, this orphan was sent to Lowood School, where she became, in time, a teacher. When she left, it was to become a governess to the ward of a certain Mr Rochester.
Jane	Mr Rivers!
St John	Mr Rochester pretended to offer honourable marriage to this young girl; but at the altar, she discovered that he had a wife still living, though insane. She left Thornfield Hall, and though Mr Rochester sought her far and wide he could get no word of her.
Jane	What of Mr Rochester? How and where is he? What is he doing? Is he well?
St John	I have the story I have just told you from a lawyer named Briggs. I know nothing of Mr Rochester, except that he must be a bad man.

Jane	You don't know him – don't pronounce an opinion upon him.
St John	Very well. You haven't asked the name of this missing governess. (*Jane is silent*) Briggs wrote to me of a Jane Eyre. I knew a Jane Elliot, who had arrived at Marsh End shortly after Jane Eyre had disappeared.
Jane	How long have you known who I am?
St John	I did not know for certain until I examined your portrait of Miss Oliver. You have forgotten yourself, and signed it with your own name.
Jane	And what does Mr Briggs want with me?
St John	Merely to tell you that your uncle, John Eyre of Madeira, is dead and has left you all his property. That you are now rich – nothing more.
Jane	Rich? How rich?
St John	Oh, a trifling amount. Twenty thousand pounds.

> *Jane* gasps in a mixture of astonishment and horror. *St John* laughs at her reaction.

St John	Why, I bring you good news and you look as if you have been found guilty of murder! Well, I shall leave you to your sorrows.
Jane	Wait! Why did Mr Briggs write to you about me?
St John	Perhaps you are not aware that my full name is St John Eyre Rivers?
Jane	But…
St John	My mother's maiden name was Eyre. She was your father's sister.
Jane	Then… my uncle John was your uncle John, who died recently leaving all his money to another distant relative…
St John	Yourself, yes.

Jane	Then we are cousins?
St John	You, I, Mary, and Diana – cousins, yes.
Jane	Oh, I am so glad!
St John	I tell you that you have twenty thousand pounds, and you are miserable. I tell you that you have three poor cousins and you are joyful. Where is your sense of proportion?
Jane	Oh, hush! What do I want with twenty thousand pounds? Do you think me greedy and ungrateful? Twenty thousand between four cousins is five thousand pounds each. Mary and Diana shall come home, and we shall live at Marsh End together.
St John	You do not know what it is to have wealth…
Jane	I know what it is to have no family. I have one now, and nothing is more important to me.
St John	Jane, I will be your brother, and my sisters your sisters, without demanding this sacrifice of you. Anyway, you may marry.
Jane	There is only one man I should ever wish to marry, and I cannot have him.
St John	That is saying too much. Yet you could put your inheritance to a better use.
Jane	Then tell me what it is.
St John	Since you began work at this school, you have done a great deal of good. Could you not devote the rest of your life to such a task?
Jane	What do you mean?
St John	I leave England in six weeks. I have taken a berth in a ship of the East India company.
Jane	May God protect you.

St John	It seems strange to me that all around me do not burn to join me in carrying the Lord's banner.
Jane	Not all have your strength of purpose.
St John	Yet there are those worthy of the work. Before I leave, it is my duty to show them where their duty lies.
Jane	Will their own hearts not show them that?
St John	What does your heart say?
Jane	It says… nothing.
St John	Then I must speak for it. Jane, come to India with me.

Jane stands up, disturbed by St John's request.

St John	God and nature have prepared you to be a missionary's wife. You were made for hard work and sacrifice, not for love.
Jane	Your… wife? If you wished a wife, why did you not marry Rosamond Oliver?
St John	Miss Oliver… the 'Rose of the World'… a missionary's wife? Ask yourself, Jane – is it likely?
Jane	But I am not fit for the work.
St John	You are right; who is fit for it? Not I; yet I have been chosen, and so have you.
Jane	You have heard a call; I have not. You would persuade me to attempt something beyond my strength.
St John	I have seen your devotion to your pupils, your hard work. You have shown that worldly wealth has no power over you. You are quiet, faithful, and courageous; very gentle and very heroic. What more is required of anyone? I trust you unreservedly; your help would be invaluable to me.
Jane	I cannot do it!

St John	You can! You have proposed that you use your wealth to set up house with my sisters, and live in idleness and content. I make a different proposal. Set aside all joys and loves of this world, and turn your face to the next. Come to India as my wife, and work with me for the glory of God.

*For a moment **Jane** is undecided.*

Jane	When first I left Thornfield, I fled temptation. For long afterwards, I hoped to die. Now I have reasons to live, and you would sentence me to a slow death under the Indian sun. Yet I could do as you ask…
St John	You could.
Jane	… except in one particular. I am ready to go to India, but not as your wife.
St John	I do not understand you.
Jane	You do not love me. You prize me as a soldier prizes a good weapon; that is all. As your sister I might go with you, not as your wife.
St John	Legally, you are not my sister. It would not do.
Jane	I will give you my energies and devotion, but not myself.
St John	Do you think God will be satisfied with half a sacrifice?
Jane	Oh! I will give my heart to God. You do not want it!
St John	We must be married; there is no other way. And after marriage, love may follow – sufficient to content us both.
Jane	(*Coldly*) I scorn your idea of love! I scorn you when you offer it.
St John	I know of nothing I have done to deserve your scorn.
Jane	St John, you are a good and a great man, but you forget the feelings and claims of little people in your determination to do what you believe to be right.

St John	(*Very gently*) Jane, your old life is behind you. A new and better one awaits. I ask you one final time, to be my wife, and help me do all things to the glory of God.
Jane	(*In torment*) Oh God! Show me, show me the path!

Mr Rochester's voice is heard very faintly, as if carried on the wind.

Mr Rochester	(*Far off*) Jane! Jane! Jane!

Jane stares wildly around seeking the voice.

St John	What is it?
Jane	Did you not hear it? A voice… a voice spoke to me… Mr Rochester's voice.
St John	(*Standing*) Jane…
Jane	(*Calling out*) I am coming to you! Where are you?
St John	Jane, you heard nothing. This is superstition. It is evil!
Jane	No. It is not evil. I know my way now. (*She calls aloud*) Wait for me! I am coming for you!

Jane rushes off stage. St John stares after her in dismay as the lights fade to blackout.

· ·

Act 5

· · · · · · ·

Scene 1

*The stage is dark and bare. From off stage there is a shout of laughter from **Bertha Mason**. The sound effect of a fire begins and builds. Thornfield Hall is ablaze*. Flames rise, and smoke billows from one wing. **Jane** and the **publican** enter on the opposite side of the stage. They face the audience but remain in shadow. **Mrs Fairfax** and **Adèle** enter quickly through the smoke.*

Mrs Fairfax   Adèle, come, child!

*She comforts **Adèle**. **Leah** rushes on stage through the smoke and joins them. **John** enters from a different direction with a bucket of water. Then **Mr Rochester** enters through the smoke.*

Mr Rochester   Leave it, John; the fire has too great a hold. You and Leah get clear!

***Grace Poole** enters running from the smoking wing. **Mr Rochester** stops her.*

Mr Rochester	Where is she? Where is my wife?
Grace Poole	She started it, sir. I must have dropped off for a minute…

>   *Mr Rochester drags a bottle from Grace Poole's pocket and flings it away.*

Mr Rochester	Drunk again, damn you! Where is she?
Grace Poole	She got into Miss Eyre's old room, sir, and set fire to the bed. I don't know where she might be now…

>   *Bertha Mason's laughter howls out once more. Mr Rochester, Grace Poole and the others look up.*

Mr Rochester	She's on the roof!

>   *He runs towards the smoke.*

John	(*Catching him*) You can't go back in there, sir!

>   *Mr Rochester throws him off and exits through the smoke. Suddenly the fire burns more fiercely. Mrs Fairfax, Adèle, Leah, and Grace Poole are driven off stage by the 'heat'. John remains looking anxiously towards the fire. The lights come up on Jane and the publican. Jane stares out into the audience, seeing the events, as the publican describes them, in her mind's eye. The sound effects fade as the publican speaks.*

Publican	Aye, (*Indicating with his hand*) that's Thornfield yonder, or what's left of it. It's a mercy as they got out alive, all save one.
Jane	Who…?
Publican	The madwoman, Mr Rochester's wife. He got all the servants out of their beds and away, but she'd climbed to the roof. I saw her: a big woman with long black hair; I could see it streaming in the flames as she stood. Waving her arms about,

she was, and shouting so's you could hear her a mile off. I saw Mr Rochester climb out beside her, and beckon her to come down, but she gave a howl and leapt, and the next minute she lay smashed on the pavement.

Jane   Dead?

Publican   Aye, miss. Dead as the stones on which her brains and blood were scattered.

Jane   And Mr Rochester?

> *The lighting and sound effects build again to a climax to suggest the collapse of the house.* **John** *rushes off stage through the smoking wing. The sound effects fade as the* **publican** *continues his story.*

Publican   As he came down the staircase, there was a terrible crash – all fell. He lay crushed under a great beam, as the fire raged around him.

> *The lighting and sound effects of the fire build again.* **John** *enters through the smoke dragging* **Mr Rochester** *with him. The lighting and sound effects fade as* **John** *attempts to comfort his injured master. The* **publican** *continues.*

Publican   They dragged him out of the ruins; though there's some say it might have been better had they left him to die. One of his hands was so crushed the doctor had to amputate it. Aye, and his eyes...

Jane   His eyes?

Publican   He was blinded; aye, stone blind is Mr Edward.

> **Mr Rochester** *lifts his sightless eyes to heaven and cries out.*

Mr Rochester   Jane! Jane! Jane!

*Jane hides her face in her hands. The lighting and sound effects of the fire fade out completely as **John** helps **Mr Rochester** from the stage. The light on **Jane** brightens. The **publican** fetches a stool and a tankard. He invites **Jane** to sit down, then starts to polish the tankard.*

Publican Of course, we never even knew there was a lunatic up at the Hall until Mr Rochester fell in love with a young lady. A governess she was, and the servants say he set store on her past everything. They never saw anybody so much in love as he was, though nobody but him thought her very handsome. A little, small thing, she was, almost like a child, they say, for I never saw her myself. Well, he would marry her, and that's when it was discovered that he had a wife already.

Jane What happened to this governess?

Publican Oh, she ran away, miss, a while before; and for all Mr Rochester sought her, as if she had been the most precious thing he had in the world, he never could hear a word of her. And so he grew savage – quite savage in his disappointment. He was never a mild man, but he grew dangerous after he lost her.

Jane Where is Mr Rochester now?

Publican He would have nobody by him after the fire. He sent his housekeeper, Mrs Fairfax, to live with friends, and sent his ward, Miss Adèle, to school.

Jane But where is he?

Publican Went to live at Ferndean, a manor house on a farm he has, about thirty miles off. Quite a desolate spot.

Jane Who is with him?

Publican Just old John and Leah; he would have no one else. He is quite broken down, they say. Now, can I get you anything, miss?

Jane (*Standing*) Yes, landlord. You can get me your pony and trap.

Publican	(*Surprised*) Pony and trap, miss? But you've only just got here. Well, if you say so. Where are you bound, miss?
Jane	To Ferndean.

The lights fade to blackout.

. . . .

Scene 2

*Ferndean. The upstage area is set with a chair, a footstool, and an occasional table. **Mr Rochester**, now blind, sits slumped in the chair, as if he has lost the will to live. The lights come up on **Jane**, downstage. She speaks to the audience.*

Jane	I turned my back on the terrible ruin of Thornfield, and arrived at Ferndean just before dark. The decaying walls of the house lay huddled under a weeping sky. All was grey, cold and desolate.

Leah enters carrying a tray, bearing a glass of water and some candles. On seeing Jane, she stops and stares.

Jane	(*To the audience*) Inside the house, I found John mending the fire, and Leah, who stared at me as if she had seen a ghost. She had with her a tray on which were a glass of water and some candles.

Jane turns to Leah.

Leah	He always has candles brought in at dark, though he is blind.

*Jane takes the tray and **Leah** exits. The lights build slightly to reveal Mr Rochester. Jane puts down the tray and lights the candles. **Mr Rochester** stirs.*

Mr Rochester	Give me the water, Leah.
Jane	Leah is in the kitchen, sir.

Mr Rochester	Who is that? Answer... speak again!
Jane	Here is your water, sir.
Mr Rochester	Am I falling into madness at last?
Jane	No, sir.

Jane takes **Mr Rochester's** *hand. He embraces her.*

Mr Rochester	I thought I heard... Is it Jane? These are her hands... this is her face...
Jane	...and this her voice. I am Jane Eyre; I have come back to you.
Mr Rochester	But I have dreamed so often that I have clasped her to my heart, and kissed her; and always, on waking, found her gone, and my vision an empty mockery.
Jane	I am no vision.
Mr Rochester	You will leave me, too; but kiss me before you go. One last kiss, Jane.

She kisses him.

Jane	There, sir!
Mr Rochester	It is you! And I thought you were lying dead in some ditch, or an outcast among strangers.
Jane	Far from it, sir. I am an independent woman now. My uncle in Madeira is dead, and he left me five thousand pounds.
Mr Rochester	Ah! Then you are real! I should never have dreamt anything as unlikely as that!
Jane	I will be your neighbour, your nurse, your housekeeper, your companion. I shall not leave you again.
Mr Rochester	My nurse! But you cannot always be my nurse, Jane: you are young. You must marry one day.

Jane	I don't care about being married.
Mr Rochester	You should care. If I were what I once was, I should try to make you care. But look at me! Branded by fire and wrecked by storm, like the old chestnut tree at Thornfield.
Jane	It's about time someone took you in hand. Look at your hair – like a lion's mane. Have you a pocket comb about you, sir?
Mr Rochester	Here.

With difficulty, **Mr Rochester** *takes out a comb.* **Jane** *sits on his knee and begins to comb his hair.*

Jane	You are more than half a goblin! I suppose your nails have grown to claws.
Mr Rochester	On this arm, I have neither hand nor nails, and my face… am I not hideous, Jane?
Jane	Very, sir. You always were, you know.
Mr Rochester	Humph! Wherever you have been, the wickedness has not been taken out of you.
Jane	Yet I have been with good people, a hundred times better than you.
Mr Rochester	Whom the deuce have you been with? Elf! Changeling! Ow!
Jane	If you twist around like that I shall pull the hair from your head. At least that should convince you that I am no spirit.
Mr Rochester	For months now I have felt nothing but hunger when I forgot to eat, or cold when I let the fire go out; but now I feel afraid.
Jane	Afraid, sir?
Mr Rochester	That you will leave as suddenly as you came, passing from my life like a shadow. Oh Jane, what did you do when you fled from Thornfield?

Jane *faces the audience.*

Jane	(*To the audience*) So I told him of my travels, and of Marsh End and my meeting with my cousins – about Mary, and Diana, and St John. He was especially interested in St John Rivers.
Mr Rochester	This St John, then, is your cousin? Do you like him?
Jane	(*Turning back to Mr Rochester*) He is a very good man. I could not help liking him.
Mr Rochester	He would be older than you, I suppose?
Jane	St John is only twenty-nine.
Mr Rochester	Still, a weedy country parson, eh?
Jane	On the contrary, a well-made man.
Mr Rochester	Uncouth in his manner, I daresay.
Jane	I never mentioned his manners, but he is quite a gentleman.
Mr Rochester	But his appearance: scrawny, chicken-necked, pinch-nosed…
Jane	St John is a very handsome man.
Mr Rochester	(*Aside*) Damn him! (*To Jane*) Perhaps you would rather not sit any longer on my knee, Miss Eyre?
Jane	Why not, Mr Rochester? (**Mr Rochester** *does not answer*) Oh, did I mention that St John asked me to marry him?
Mr Rochester	(*Sulkily*) You are making that up to vex me.
Jane	I beg your pardon, I am not. He was very clear on the point; quite as insistent as you ever were.
Mr Rochester	Miss Eyre, I repeat, you can leave me. Why do you remain perched on my knee when I have given you notice to quit?
Jane	Because I am comfortable there.

Mr Rochester	No, Jane, you are not comfortable there, because your heart is not with me; it is with this cousin, this St John. You must go your own way, with the husband you have chosen.
Jane	Well, so I shall. St John Rivers is not my husband, nor ever could be. He does not love me; I do not love him. He is good and great, but as cold and severe as an iceberg. You need not be jealous of St John. All my heart is yours, sir. It belongs to you, and with you it will remain for ever.

> *They embrace; then **Jane** leads **Mr Rochester** forward and speaks to the audience. As the characters are mentioned in her narrative, they take their place on the stage. During **Jane's** final speeches, the characters she names assemble to form a final tableau.*

Jane	And so, we were married. Mrs Fairfax came to cry over us both, and wish us joy. Adèle came back from school, and danced at my wedding even more gaily than she had once danced for the mock wedding of Mr Rochester and Blanche Ingram.

> ***Blanche Ingram** glares disapprovingly at Jane and Mr Rochester. **St John Rivers** enters, reading a letter, which he then crumples.*

Jane	(*To the audience*) How St John received the news of my marriage to Mr Rochester, I don't know. He never answered the letter in which I told him of it. Six months later he wrote to me from India; but in all his letters since, he has never once mentioned Mr Rochester's name. Edward remained blind for the first two years of our marriage, but one morning, he asked me…
Mr Rochester	Jane, have you a glittering ornament round your neck?
Jane	(*Turning to him*) Yes.
Mr Rochester	And have you a pale-blue dress on?

*Jane embraces **Mr Rochester**, then turns back to speak to the audience.*

Jane   Even now, he sees little distinctly, and cannot read and write much. But the sky is no longer a blank to him, nor the earth a void. We daily thank God that in the midst of judgement, he has remembered mercy. Mary and Diana are both married; we see them often. St John has never married; he will never marry now. His labours draw to their close, but no fear of death will darken his last hour. His eyes will be fixed on heaven, and his sure hope of an incorruptible crown. There is a new tree in our garden at Ferndean: a cutting from the old chestnut tree at Thornfield Hall. It has grown into a handsome sapling, straight and strong. Now it is putting out new leaves; for however hard the winter and however deep the frost, that which survives grows stronger; and spring will always come again.

The lights fade.

Activities

About the Author

Charlotte Brontë was born in Thornton, near Bradford, on 21 April 1816. Her father, Patrick Brontë, was a clergyman in the church of England, and her mother, Maria (born Branwell) came from Cornwall. Patrick and Maria Brontë had six children; five girls: Maria, Elizabeth, Charlotte, Emily, and Anne, and one boy: Patrick Branwell.

In 1820, the Brontës moved to Haworth near Keighley in Yorkshire, where they lived in the parsonage. The countryside around Haworth was wild, bleak moorland plagued by rain and gusting winds – conditions which probably contributed to the poor health of Mrs Brontë and her children.

In 1821, Charlotte's mother died. Her aunt, Elizabeth Branwell, travelled from the south of England to look after the children. However, she found it impossible to adapt to the harsh climate of the Yorkshire moors and spent much of her time in her bedroom. Charlotte's father also spent much of his time on his own. He was an eccentric character who wanted to make his children 'hardy and indifferent to the pleasures of eating and dress'.

In 1824, Maria, Elizabeth, Charlotte, and Emily were sent to boarding school at Cowen Bridge. The conditions at the school were poor and both Maria and Elizabeth developed consumption (an infectious disease causing the wasting of body tissue, especially in the lungs). They both died in 1825 and Charlotte and Emily returned home to Haworth.

Life at the parsonage was not easy for the remaining Brontë children, and they were often left to entertain themselves. They ran free on the moors above Haworth and found escape in a fantasy world, by inventing the imaginary lands of Great Glass Town, Gondal and Angria. They made up dozens of stories and poems about these lands and their inhabitants, recording them in minute handwriting in tiny home-made books.

One of the miniature books produced by Charlotte Brontë as a child

In 1831, Charlotte went to Roe Head School, near Mirfield, first as a pupil and then later as a pupil-teacher. On leaving the school, she spent a couple of years working as a governess, and then in 1842, she and Emily went to Brussels to gain further qualifications. They became students at a school run by Constantine Héger and, a year later, Charlotte became a teacher there. During this time she fell in love with Professor Héger, Madame Héger's husband. Her love was not returned and so Charlotte travelled home to Haworth and wrote a novel based on her experiences called *The Professor*. It was rejected for publication, but Charlotte was encouraged to write **Jane Eyre**, which was published in 1847.

In September 1848, Charlotte's brother, Branwell died. Emily, suffering from consumption, died later the same year, in December. Anne's health also deteriorated during this time and she died five months after Emily.

Charlotte remained with her father at Haworth and wrote more novels. She published *Shirley* in 1849 and *Villette* in 1853. She had several offers of marriage and eventually married her father's curate, Arthur Nicholls, in 1854. Tragically, the marriage lasted less than a year as Charlotte died in March 1855. Her first book, *The Professor*, was the last to be published; it came out two years after her death, in 1857. Today, Charlotte Brontë is acknowledged as a great writer and a major influence on the development of the English novel.

This is an extract from a letter written by Charlotte on 6 March 1843 while she was working as a teacher in Brussels. She is writing to her friend Ellen Nussey. The illustration gives an interesting insight into Charlotte's view of herself. She is the small, rather odd figure on the left and Ellen is the tall, graceful lady on the right. The man is Ellen's suitor.
Can you find any links between these drawings of Charlotte and Ellen and any characters in **Jane Eyre**?
(See Autobiography on p.111)

Jane Eyre – The Novel

Read

When Charlotte, Emily and Anne began to write, female authors were rare. The sisters believed that their books would not be taken seriously if people knew they were women, so they adopted pen-names to disguise this fact. Charlotte took the name Currer Bell, while Emily and Anne adopted the names Ellis and Acton Bell.

Their first success came in 1846, with the publication of *Poems: by Currer, Ellis and Acton Bell*. **Jane Eyre** was published the following year in 1847 also under the pseudonym Currer Bell. Emily's novel *Wuthering Heights* and Anne's *Agnes Grey* were also published in the same year.

At the time it was thought that the three novels were the work of a single writer, so in 1848, Charlotte and Anne went to London to prove their identities. In the same year, Anne's second novel, *The Tenant of Wildfell Hall*, was published. Less than a year later, Branwell, Emily and Anne Brontë were all dead.

Critical Reactions

Read and Discuss

Jane Eyre was an immediate success with the reading public. Lady Cavendish described it in her diary as 'the most powerful novel I ever read', and another novelist, Mrs Oliphant, called it a 'revolution' and its author a 'dangerous little person'.

The Brontë sisters

The reaction of the critics was mixed. Some thought the book was spiritually uplifting and set high moral standards: 'Lose not a day in sending for it', said one critic, adding that **Jane Eyre** portrays a life 'both noble and sad…a lesson in duty and self reliance' and that its 'deep, significant reality' would make 'a deep and permanent impression'.

Another critic commented: 'There can be no question but that **Jane Eyre** is a very clever book. Indeed it is a book of decided power. The thoughts are true, sound and original; and the style, though rude and uncultivated here and there, is resolute, straightforward, and to the purpose…'

But others thought **Jane Eyre** dangerously immoral, and accused it of being anti-Christian, vulgar and subversive.

One American reviewer condemned the 'profanity, brutality and slang' of Mr Rochester's character and speech, describing them as 'torpedo shocks to the nervous system'. While another reviewer remarked: 'A book more unfeminine…it would be hard to find in the annals of female authorship. Throughout there is masculine power, breadth, and shrewdness, combined with masculine hardness, coarseness, and freedom of expression.'

'Mr Rochester is a man who deliberately and secretly seeks to violate the laws both of God and man, and yet we are bound half our lady readers are enchanted with him for a model of generosity and honour…' was the response of another critic.

1   Which side would you agree with?
2   Do you agree with any of the individual points raised by the reviewers? Why do you think some of them were so shocked by the story?
3   Do we still find **Jane Eyre** shocking today?

Autobiography

Research and Discuss

Many writers use their own lives as the basis for their writing.

1   Try and build on the portrait of Charlotte Brontë that appears on pages 108–109. Find out more about:
   ● her physical appearance
   ● her upbringing
   ● her experiences at school
   ● her sisters
   ● the jobs she took on leaving school
   ● her marriage
2   Using your research, discuss in small groups what incidents in **Jane Eyre** could be considered to be based on Charlotte's real life experiences.
3   Share your ideas with the rest of the class.

Write

1   Write about an incident from your own school life. This could be a happy or sad moment. Like Charlotte Brontë, you may wish to add details to the story to make it more exciting or dramatic. You could then use this incident as a basis for a rehearsed improvisation (see page 122).
2   Imagine that you are writing a book in which one of the major characters is a slightly disguised version of yourself. Write a description of yourself as the hero or heroine of your book.

The World of Jane Eyre

Social Class

Read

In Charlotte Brontë's time, social positions were very rigidly defined. A person's position in society was usually determined by:
- birth
- wealth.

People were expected to know their place in society, but that place could change:
- downwards, through disgrace or poverty, or
- upwards, through marriage or becoming rich.

Research

1   Divide into small groups. Each group has responsibility for collecting information about life within a particular social class in the early and middle Nineteenth century in Britain. Choose from the list below, but make sure that all four areas are covered by at least one group.
- the aristocracy and upper classes
- the middle classes
- the working classes
- the poor and criminal classes

2   Then each group must research the lifestyle of a representative person from their chosen social class.

3   Finally, using this information, each group must deliver a report back to the rest of the class, in one or more of the following ways:
- as a talk
- as a written report
- as a wall display using maps, pictures, charts, photocopies, and written captions
- as a role play (you could have interviews with nineteenth-century characters, etc)
- as a radio programme (record this on cassette tape)
- as a TV documentary programme (record this on video tape).

Read and Discuss

1   Divide into pairs or small groups. Each group must examine one of the characters, or group of characters, listed below.

Mr Rochester	Mr Briggs, the lawyer
Mrs Reed and her children	Rosamond Oliver
Grace Poole	Mr Brocklehurst
Mary, Diana and St John Rivers	Bessie
Blanche and Mary Ingram	John and Leah
Lady Lynn	Mrs Fairfax
Miss Temple	Colonel Dent

Hannah   Bertha Mason
Adèle Varens   Mr Wood, the clergyman
Jane's uncle, John Eyre of Madeira   Helen Burns

2   To which social class does your character belong?

3   Find evidence in the playscript to back up your opinions. It may be helpful
     to record your findings on a chart. For example, you might begin a chart
     for Mr Rochester like this:

CHARACTER	CLASS	EVIDENCE
Mr Rochester	Upper	Act 2, Scene 3
		Mrs Fairfax calls him 'the master'
		He orders Mrs Fairfax and Jane about

4   Each group should then report its findings to the rest of the class.

Jane Eyre's Social Position

It is difficult to see where Jane fits into the class system of Victorian
England. Her position in society rises and falls throughout the playscript.
Often, her social standing is revealed though the eyes of other characters in
the way they treat her and what they think of her situation or employment.

1   Look back at the following episodes in Jane's life:
     ● living with the Reeds at Gateshead Hall
     ● going as a charity girl to Lowood School
     ● becoming a teacher at Lowood
     ● becoming a governess at Thornfield Hall
     ● meeting Mr Rochester's houseguests
     ● accepting Mr Rochester's offer of marriage
     ● between leaving Thornfield Hall and arriving at Marsh End
     ● working as a teacher at Morton School
     ● inheriting money from John Eyre
     ● marrying Mr Rochester

2   Working in small groups and using what you know about the class system
     in Victorian England, decide which social class Jane belongs to during these
     periods of her life.

3   Join up with another group and compare your findings. Consider the
     following questions:
     ● Were there times when it was difficult to place Jane in a particular
       social class?
     ● Did you disagree on any of your decisions?

4   Report back to the rest of the class.

The Place of Women in Jane Eyre

Read

In the England of the 1840s, women did not have the opportunities they have today. There were no women doctors, or lawyers; no female journalists or managers; no businesswomen, no women in politics or the armed forces. There was an idea amongst the wealthy that work for women was not respectable.

However, some women had to work to support themselves and often their families too. The options open to these women were limited. We see an example of this when Jane leaves Thornfield Hall at the end of Act 3. We later learn that before she is taken in by the Rivers family, she asks a woman she meets on the road if there is any work available locally. The woman is not encouraging: the village already has enough dressmakers, she knows of no place requiring servants, and Mr Oliver does not employ women in his factory. As there is no social security system for Jane to fall back on, her failure to find work is almost the death of her.

Rich and poor women in Nineteenth-century society. The photograph (right) shows a poor family making brushes.

List

Here is a list of the paid employment available to the women in the play:
- teacher
- governess
- housekeeper
- servant
- nurse

1   Make your own list of all the characters who are employed to do these jobs in the play.

2   Then, write a description of what each character does. You might want to set the whole activity out like the example below.

OCCUPATION	CHARACTER	DESCRIPTION
Housekeeper	Mrs Fairfax	Keeps keys to the stores Supervizes John and Leah Makes Thornfield ready for Mr Rochester and his guests

3   Are there any female characters in the play who do not have paid jobs?

4   If so, who are they and how do they spend their time? Add this information to your list.

Talk and
Write

1   Divide into small groups and discuss one or more of the following questions:
- What opportunities do men have in the play that women do not?
- Were the strict moral standards of Charlotte Brontë's time applied to men and women equally?
- How have women's roles in society changed since Charlotte Brontë's time?

2   Write down your findings.

3   Then share them with the rest of the class.

Characters

Jane Eyre

List and Discuss 1 Make a spidergraph of words that describe Jane Eyre. Look for examples in the playscript that back up the words you have chosen. For instance, if you think that Jane is kind, find an incident in the play that supports this viewpoint. You may wish to have separate lists for Jane as a child and Jane as an adult. The example below will get you started.

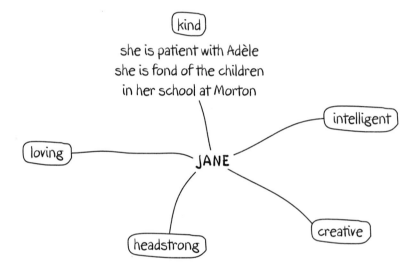

2 As a class, share all your findings and produce a large spidergraph which can be displayed on your classroom wall.

Viewpoints

List and discuss Throughout the play, Jane is judged by other people.

1 Look through the playscript to find out what the other characters say about Jane, and make a list of these comments. It has been started for you below:

WHAT THEY SAY	WHO SAYS IT	WHEN THEY SAY IT
'You are less than a servant'	Mrs Reed	Act I, Scene 2
'Jane Eyre is not a liar'	Miss Temple	Act I, Scene 3

2 Present your findings to the rest of the class and discuss whether these are fair comments.

Mr Rochester

List and Discuss 1 Make a spidergraph of words that describe Mr Rochester. Look for examples in the playscript that back up the words you have chosen. For instance, if you think that Mr Rochester is a bully, find an incident in the play that supports this viewpoint. You could use the example below as a starting point.

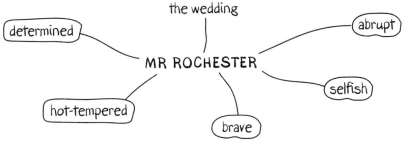

2 As a class, share all your findings and produce a large spidergraph which can be displayed on your classroom wall.

Write Imagine you are Mr Rochester. Write a diary which starts on the day of your first meeting with Jane (Act 2, Scene 2), and ends with your proposal of marriage to her (Act 3, Scene 2). For example, the first entry might begin:

> Nearly had my neck broken for me today. I was riding towards Thornfield when some female appeared out of the mist and made my horse slip on the ice, so that I fell off. It turned out she was Adèle's governess (I'd completely forgotten that I told Mrs Fairfax to find one). I was pretty short-tempered with her, but she was quite calm and not offended by my snapping. She is a very ordinary young woman to look at, very thin and pale, but there is something about her that interests me...

You could split this activity up by working in groups of four. Each group member could write one section of the diary covered by the acts and scenes listed below:

- Act 1, Scenes 2 and 3
- Act 2, Scene 2 to Scene 4
- Act 2, Scene 5 to Act 3, Scene 1
- Act 3, Scene 2

Courtship

Talk and Write

Mr Rochester quickly falls in love with Jane, and Jane with him. In two columns, write down what difficulties you think stand in the way of their relationship. The list has been started for you.

REASONS WHY MR ROCHESTER CANNOT DECLARE HIS LOVE FOR JANE

REASONS WHY JANE CANNOT DECLARE HER LOVE FOR MR ROCHESTER

He is older than Jane

She is Mr Rochester's servant

Separation

List

Make a list of the things that happen individually to Jane and Mr Rochester between Jane's departure from Thornfield (end of Act 3), and her return to Mr Rochester at Ferndean (Act 5).
The list for Jane might begin:

JANE
wanders cold and hungry across the moors for several days

While the list for Mr Rochester might begin:

MR ROCHESTER
tries everything he can to find Jane, but fails

Discuss

How do these events help to break down the barriers that separate Jane and Mr Rochester? Share your ideas with the rest of the class.

Write

1   Imagine you are Jane. You have just run away from Thornfield and are recovering at Marsh End. Write a monologue, describing your thoughts and feelings at this time. Read this out to the rest of the class.

2   Imagine you are Mr Rochester. It is a month since Jane ran away from Thornfield. You have found out that Jane is at Marsh End. Write a letter to her trying to persuade her to come back.

Debate

Talk

Arrange a class debate on the question: 'Should Jane have married Mr Rochester?'

1   Choose a group to argue 'Yes' and a group to argue 'No'.

2   Each group must decide its response to a number of questions, including the following:

   • Is Mr Rochester a good man or a bad one?
   • Can excuses be made for Mr Rochester's behaviour?
   • What options are open to Jane?
   • Does she make the right choices?
   • Why does she make these choices?
   • Are these the right reasons?

3   Both sides then put forward their arguments.

4   Other members of the class now have the opportunity to ask questions or make comments.

5   Finally, a vote is taken.

You can record your debate on audiotape or videotape if you wish.

An artist's view of Rochester's first appearance in the story

The Gothic Novel

Read

Gothic novels are stories of the macabre and supernatural. They are usually set in haunted castles, graveyards or wild places. The characters in such novels are often strange and sometimes exotic. Extreme weather conditions and unexplainable noises add to the atmosphere, and there is usually some sort of mystery that is central to the plot.

The first Gothic novel is considered to be *The Castle of Otranto* by Horace Walpole which was written in 1746. But perhaps the most famous of all Gothic novels is *Frankenstein* by Mary Shelley written in 1818.

The popularity of Gothic novels grew during the late-Eighteenth and early-Nineteenth centuries. Many writers during this period included some gothic elements in their work and Charlotte Brontë was no exception. (See What the Adapters Say, page 126.)

List

1 Make a list of things that help to make a 'spooky' tale. If you have read any Gothic novels, you can include elements from them in your list.

Below is an example to get you started.

PLACES	PEOPLE	ATMOSPHERE
A lonely castle	A mysterious Count	Night time
A graveyard	A young girl	Wind and rain

2 Share your findings with the rest of the class.

3 Divide into pairs. Using your lists as a guide, read through the playscript and pick out the 'gothic' elements.

4 Make a list of these.

5 Share your findings with the rest of the class.

Discuss

As a class, discuss all or some of the following points.
- Are the gothic elements in **Jane Eyre** essential to the plot?
- What do these elements bring to the play?
- Why do you think Charlotte Brontë included them in **Jane Eyre**?

The Gothic Today

Discuss

Unexplained mysteries and the supernatural are still popular today. Films and television series such as the *X Files* are watched worldwide. Series of books like Point Horror and Goosebumps sell in their millions.

1 In small groups, discuss the following points:
- What 'spooky' books or television series do members of your class read and watch?
- Why do they watch and read these?
- Do people like being scared? If so, why?

2 Share your ideas with the rest of the class.

Talk

Many people have their own 'spooky' tale to tell. For example, walking home through a graveyard at night, being in the house on your own and hearing strange noises, etc.

1 Does anyone in your class have a tale to tell?

2 If so, get them to tell it, but before they begin, discuss the techniques they can use to build up a 'spooky' atmosphere while telling their tale.

3 Afterwards talk about their tale – both the story and the way it was told. Can you suggest any improvements?

Write

Write your own story that includes 'gothic' elements in it. You could base it on your own experiences or make it up. Don't copy one from a book you have read or a film you have seen, try to come up with your own ideas.

Mary Shelley's
Frankenstein

The X Files

Drama

You can use the following drama techniques to help you to explore the play further.

Improvisation

You are given a situation to work on in groups. Using your own words you act out a scene which shows what you think about the subject. There are two main types of improvisation.

Planned: in this you are given time to prepare your work by talking with your friends and trying out your ideas. When you have practised your work and are satisfied with it, you show it to other people.

Instant: in this you are given a character and a situation, but you are not given any time to prepare. You must start the improvisation straight away.

Improvise   1   In pairs, improvise a scene in which a pupil is wrongly accused of doing something bad by a teacher. How can the pupil persuade the teacher that they are innocent and the teacher is wrong?

2   In small groups, improvise a scene in which a person discovers a terrible secret about their best friend.

Still Image

A still image is like a photograph. Any number of people may be in the image. A situation is chosen and the group must produce a frozen picture as if they had just been captured on film by a photographer or on canvas by a painter. You may wish to choose just one image or use a series of images to tell a story.

Thought Tapping

This helps us to understand what the characters in a still image are thinking. In turn, each member of the group says what their character was thinking at the moment the 'photograph' was taken.

Still Image   1   In small groups, choose three different moments from the play and create a still image for each of these.

Thought   2   Each character in the image speaks a thought that they are thinking at the
Tapping   moment captured by the image. Show the rest of the class. Can they guess who your characters are and which part of the play your image comes from? How did they work it out?

Hot Seating

When a member of the group has played or is about to play a character in an improvisation, a role play or a written play, they can be put in the 'hot seat'. This means that other members of the group can ask them questions, and they must answer them **in the character** of their chosen person.

Hot Seating

As the play progresses, Jane's character changes. We can use hot seating to help us to explore and understand this development.

1   Prepare a list of questions that you would like to ask Jane when she first arrives at Thornfield. You can use the following questions as a starting point.
   ● Is she pleased to be away from Lowood?
   ● What were her favourite times there?
   ● What were her worst times?
   ● What are her views of the Reed family?
   ● Is she looking forward to meeting Mr Rochester?
   ● What are her thoughts about Adèle and Mrs Fairfax?

2   Choose a member of the class to take the role of Jane and 'hot seat' them, using your list of questions.

3   When you have finished hot seating, discuss the answers that 'Jane' gave.

4   Now imagine that it is the end of the play. Prepare a different set of questions to ask Jane. You might want to consider these listed below.

   ● How has she changed as a person since she left school?
   ● How have her views changed?
   ● What does she think now about the other characters?
   ● What has she learnt from her experiences?
   ● Is she happy?

5   Choose another member of the class to play the role of Jane and take the hot seat.

6   Hot seat other major characters from the play.

7   You may wish to hot seat some of the minor characters and try to discover if there is more to them than meets the eye. For example, do characters like Mrs Reed have a sympathetic side?

Judgement Chair

This activity gives you the chance to speak your mind about characters in the play and 'pass judgement' on them.

1   Choose a person to take on the part of one of the characters in the play.

2   Place a chair in front of the class.

3   The chosen person sits on this chair.

4   Take it in turns to stand up and tell the character what you think about them.

You can give these opinions as yourself or as another character in the play. For example, if Mrs Reed is the character in the judgement chair, you could take the part of Jane and say: 'I'm Jane. I've always hated you; you are selfish and narrow minded.'

You may wish to take the part of a character who does not appear in the play, for example, Jane's uncle, John Eyre, or Mr Oliver, Rosamond's father.

Charades

Read

The parlour game of charades is still popular today. It is perhaps more commonly known as 'Give us a Clue'. Individuals have to act out the title of a film, book, TV programme, song or play without speaking.

In Charlotte Brontë's day, the game of charades was slightly different. The words acted out were not titles of television programmes or films (there weren't any!) but individual words.

The acting out of these words could be very elaborate. Each syllable of the word had to be guessed, and players often used costumes and props in their improvisation.

In the novel, the word that Mr Rochester acts out is 'Bridewell' (which means a type of prison), but as this word is rarely used today, it was changed in the play to 'bridegroom'.

Play

Organize a game of charades. Instead of using titles of books, films or plays, choose individual words to act out. You will find this easier to do if you choose words that break down into simpler ones, for example:

- deadwood
- racetrack
- superman
- buttonhole
- lifestyle
- newspaper

Staging

Putting on the Play

Read and Design

Read What the Adapters Say, pages 126–127, and A Note on the Set, page 6. Using the information on these pages, design a set for a production of **Jane Eyre** to take place at your school. You could do this by making a 'junk model' out of bits of paper, card, wire, scrap fabric, etc. Remember that actors will have to stand on your real set and the audience will have to see them!

Slow Motion

Read

Some of the stage directions in this play ask the actors to take part in stage fighting. These instances include: the throwing of a book by John Reed; the fight between Jane and John Reed; and Bertha Mason attacking Richard Mason and Mr Rochester in the attic.

Unless you have been trained by a professional, stage fighting can be very dangerous. A way round this is to present the fight scenes in 'slow motion'. A good exercise for developing the skills of acting in slow motion is to play a sport. For example, you could throw a basketball to each other as normal. After several minutes, remove the ball from play and pretend that it is still there. After a few minutes of this, slow every movement down until you are playing in slow motion. You will need to think about the following things:

- points of balance
- the detail of your movement
- details of expression (face and gesture)
- the steady rhythm of movement.

This exercise can be developed to include any sport or physical activity. These skills may then be transferred to the appropriate scene in the play. The slow motion moves should be worked out (choreographed) and practised until they are convincing.

Poster

Design

Design a poster for a production of **Jane Eyre**. You will need to think about the following things:

- what information you wish to convey
- how to make the poster eye-catching
- what images you want to use. For example, what moments from the play are particularly dramatic? What characters should appear? etc.

What the Adapters Say

Read

When we adapted *A Tale of Two Cities* for the Oxford Playscripts series, we had to make a lot of changes. We had to cut characters, change the order of events and get rid of scenes from the book or merge them together. However, one part of the book we didn't need to change much was the dialogue. There is a good reason for this. Charles Dickens loved the theatre (he was an actor and producer himself) and this shows in his dialogue which is dramatic, and meant to be spoken. His characters speak like real people, using the words and patterns of everyday speech in Victorian times.

With **Jane Eyre** though, we had a problem. Charlotte Brontë's dialogue is meant to be read, not spoken. This is partly because the author is writing in the style of a Gothic novel. Gothic writing is spooky writing; everything is meant to be very dark and mysterious, and characters, plot and dialogue are very wordy and over-elaborate. Try speaking some of the dialogue from the book aloud, and you'll see what we mean. Here are some examples.

'And these dreams weigh on your spirits now, Jane, when I am close to you? Little nervous subject! forget visionary woe, and think only of real happiness!'

(Mr Rochester)

'Now, now good people, don't press upon me. Really, your organs of wonder and incredulity are easily excited...'

(Blanche Ingram)

'Fancy me yielding and melting, as I am doing: human love rising like a freshly opened fountain in my mind and overflowing with sweet inundation all the field I have so carefully...prepared... And now it is deluged with a nectarous flood – the young germs swamped – delicious poison cankering them...'

(St John Rivers)

This is all grand, ringing stuff, and it reads very well, but it's not how people talk (even in Charlotte Brontë's time) so it's no use in a play. For this reason, we had to change the dialogue from the novel to make it easier for the actors to say and for a modern audience to understand, without making it too modern and without losing the sense of 'period'.

Once we had thought about the dialogue, we then had to turn our attention to the plot. In adapting Charlotte Brontë's novel, we might have chosen to concentrate on the relationship between Jane and Mr Rochester, as a number of film and television adaptations have done. If we'd done this, we would simply have been giving you a love story.

However, this wouldn't have been a fair reflection on the book, which is Jane's story. Mr Rochester doesn't even appear for over 100 pages, and he disappears from the book later for another 100.

We decided that as much as possible of what happens in the novel should happen in our script, too. However, when we tried to do this, we found we had a play that would take about six hours to perform. We decided we'd have to cheat. Everything important that happens in the novel would happen in the play too, but not necessarily in the same order.

Having read the playscript, you might find it interesting to see how the characters speak and the events unfold in Charlotte Brontë's novel.

Read and Write

Adaptation Activity

You may want to have a go at adapting a section of the novel yourselves. Try the scene in Chapter 3 when Mr Lloyd (the apothecary) comes to visit Jane after her collapse in the Red room. Use the playscript as a model for setting out your adaptation, and begin with Mr Lloyd's lines:
'Come here, Miss Jane: your name is Jane, is it not?'

Further Reading

You may want to read Charlotte Brontë's other novels, *Villette*, *Shirley*, and *The Professor*, or find out more about Charlotte and her family:

Biography: *The Life of Charlotte Brontë* by Mrs Gaskell
Background: *The Brontës: The Critical Heritage* Ed. Miriam Allott

The Parsonage at Howarth. It is now a museum devoted to the lives and work of the Brontës.

Plays in this series include:

Across the Barricades   ISBN 0 19 831272 5
  Joan Lingard   adapted by David Ian Neville

The Bonny Pit Laddie   ISBN 0 19 831278 4
  *Frederick Grice   adapted by David Spraggon Williams
                  with Frank Green*

The Burston School Strike   ISBN 0 19 831274 1
  Roy Nevitt

The Canterbury Tales   ISBN 0 19 831293 8
  Geoffrey Chaucer   adapted by Martin Riley

Carrie's War   ISBN 0 19 831295 4
  Nina Bawden   adapted by Robert Staunton

The Demon Headmaster   ISBN 0 19 831270 9
  Gillian Cross   adapted by Adrian Flynn

Frankenstein   ISBN 0 19 831267 9
  Mary Shelley   adapted by Philip Pullman

Hot Cakes   ISBN 0 19 831273 3
  Adrian Flynn

Jane Eyre   ISBN 0 19 831296 2
  Charlotte Brontë   adapted by Steve Barlow and Steve Skidmore

Johnny and the Dead   ISBN 0 19 831294 6
  Terry Pratchett   adapted by Stephen Briggs

Paper Tigers   ISBN 0 19 831268 7
  Steve Barlow and Steve Skidmore

A Question of Courage   ISBN 0 19 831271 7
  Marjorie Darke   adapted by Bill Lucas and Brian Keaney

Smith   ISBN 0 19 831297 0
  Leon Garfield   adapted by Robert Staunton

A Tale of Two Cities   ISBN 0 19 831292 X
  Charles Dickens   adapted by Steve Barlow and Steve Skidmore

Tess of the D'Urbervilles   ISBN 0 19 831439 6
  Thomas Hardy   adapted by David Calcutt

The Turbulent Term of Tyke Tiler   ISBN 0 19 831269 5
  adapted from her own novel by Gene Kemp